on the road home
it was suddenly

(NEW WRITING SCOTLAND 19)

Edited by

MOIRA BURGESS
and
JANET PAISLEY

with Kevin MacNeil (Gaelic Adviser)

Association for Scottish Literary Studies

Association for Scottish Literary Studies
c/o Department of Scottish History, 9 University Gardens
University of Glasgow, Glasgow G12 8QH
www.asls.org.uk

First published 2002

British Library Cataloguing in Publication Data

A CIP record for this book is available
from the British Library

ISBN 0–948877–47–2

Published with assistance from

Typeset by Roger Booth Associates, Hassocks, West Sussex

Printed by Bell & Bain Ltd, Glasgow

CONTENTS

INTRODUCTION

Last year was the first of my three as editor of New Writing Scotland. Moira Burgess, on her second, showed me the ropes. Half the submission arrives in spring disguised as a cardboard box, large. Divided by weight, the other half simultaneously chaps the co-editor's door. It's a daunting guest, settled heavily on thick haunches in the hall. The desire to read packs and leaves town. I prowl around it, taking weeks of deep breaths. Then I pounce and the marathon starts. Piles of Nos, maybes, ehms, and Yesses sprout on coffee table, carpet, floor. The yesses grow slowly, as do the nos. It takes at least two culls to produce the required long list. Now, the swap.

I re-pack the box, nos at the bottom, maybes next, ehms on top. The yesses are stowed in a carrier. Bearing it, I meet Moira for coffee in Glasgow. With all the panache of spies in a cold war thriller, we casually arrive with one bag and leave with another. Once home, the reading starts again. This time we mercilessly reduce each other's long list to a short list, all the time hoping that our partner in crime isn't wantonly tossing aside our personal favourites from the first round. Just as summer arrives, I pack the car with initial submission box, those rejected from Moira's long list and my short list. The neighbours think I'm off on holiday. Instead it's seconds out at Moira's place (tea, coffee, biscuits and cat, with the promise of a take-away tea when the bout's over), and our stravaigin Gaelic editor, Kevin MacNeil, as referee.

We do not come to blows. All those Moira was ready to fight for have survived on my short-list. Those I would have battled to retain are on hers. We debate a few that hover on the borderline but by tea-time, we're satisfied. More than. New Writing Scotland is the one annual showcase of the best in Scottish contemporary writing. It's the flag of a healthy literary scene, with new writing from weel kent names alongside fresh voices and some first publication. Read anonymously, it's without prejudice, unfair bias, favouritism or cronyism. Every piece has to be well-made, powerful, original and packing enough punch to win its place from a jostling crowd of contenders.

Moira's stint as editor ends with this edition. We had a lot of fun and some unforgettable moments. She's due my thanks, for keeping me on track, for the hospitality and humour, the generosity of spirit and intellect. Oh, and the swansong. Volume 19. It's a knock-out.

Janet Paisley
January 2002

NEW WRITING SCOTLAND 21

Submissions are invited for the twentieth annual volume of *New Writing Scotland*, to be published in 2003, from writers resident in Scotland or Scots by birth or upbringing. Poetry, drama, short fiction or other creative prose may be submitted but not full-length plays or novels, though self-contained extracts are acceptable. The work must be neither previously published nor accepted for publication and may be in any of the languages of Scotland.

Submissions should be typed, double-spaced, on one side of the paper only and the sheets secured at the top-left corner. Prose pieces should carry an approximate word-count. You should provide a covering letter, clearly marked with your name and address. **Please do <u>not</u> put your name or other details on the individual works.** If you would like to receive an acknowledge-ment of receipt of your manuscript, please enclose a stamped addressed postcard. If you would like your submissions returned, you should enclose a stamped addressed envelope with sufficient postage. Submissions should be sent by **31 January 2003**, in an A4 envelope marked for my attention, to the address below. We are sorry but we cannot accept sub-missions by fax or e-mail.

Please be aware that we have limited space in each edition, and therefore shorter pieces are more suitable – although longer items of exceptional quality may still be included. A maximum length of 3,500 words is suggested. Please send no more than two short stories and no more than six poems.

Duncan Jones
Managing Editor, *New Writing Scotland*
ASLS
c/o Department of Scottish History
9 University Gardens
University of Glasgow
Glasgow G12 8QH
Tel: +44 (0)141 330 5309

Margaret Beveridge

SPEEDY DELIVERY – VERBAL ESTIMATE

Yeh, fuckin' swimming pool in here. I think your waters have definitely broken. Let's have a look. Where's my torch? (Muffled) You've had some cowboys in here! It wasn't a homer last time was it? Who was it? One of those 'community' mid-wives? (Taps speculum thoughtfully against teeth then inserts) These piles are completely blocking your back passage, they'll have to go. Bloody hell, these varicose veins need stripping. And this pelvic floor is going to collapse – bladder's hanging by a thread. How long have you had that leak? Not much room in here... whole wall of this womb's about to come away. You don't mind if the boys have a look. Doing an SQA module in Obs and Gynae. Brilliant...cut the training time down from five years to forty hours. Look at the tear in this perineum, just left to heal naturally, for fuck's sake. You've been stitched up, love, metaphorically speaking, that is. (muttering) Fuckin' DIY births. Fuckin' Sheila Kitzinger has a lot to answer for. Should leave it to the fuckin' experts. We've got the tools for it... (louder) Leave it to the experts, love. What does your husband think?

Need to get you down the ante-natal unit ASAP. Can't do anything here, don't have the equipment (whistling through teeth and shaking head). This time of the year, you're looking at the middle of next week. Don't get excited, love. What makes you think that was a contraction? Just leave everything to us. If push comes to shove, best I could do is leave one of the lads with you. Jim's still looking for a competence in live birth... (aside) and tie off the fuckin' cord this time. Get some plastic sheeting? Now if you go private...cash in hand, get the lads on to it right away... Could do you a nice Caesarean section, no extra cost. (pause) Labour's extra of course. Probably need some cosmetic work afterwards. Pal of mine, plastic surgeon down the private hospital, he'll see you all right. (leers meaning-fully at the group of students) Can't just paper over the cracks these days, can we lads? (students snicker obligingly)

Be back in half an hour. The gear's in the ambulance, can't shift you without it. More than my job's worth. ...parked three streets away. Fuckin' traffic wardens. May as well have lunch while we're at it. C'mon, lads. You just keep your legs open, love, so we can let ourselves back in.

Nick Brooks

JACK DANIEL'S THE FRENCH WAY

It was meant to be Ria's thirty-eighth on the coming Monday n
she says to Cherie,
    Think I'll make thirty-nine?
    n Cherie couldnae honestly tell her aye. What were ye
meant to say? Ria knew the score n everybody was gaunnae
miss her n that – but she'd become totally like a sister to Cherie.
    Cherie made a joke instead of answering:
    Never mind, she would give Toots n Rodin a good home.
Toots was the Jack Russell terrier. Rodin was the cat. Toots was
mostly white but with these wee black socks on his feet. Lovely
wee thing so he was. Rodin was just kind of – fluffy.
    Watch yerself, hon – keep yer legs covered! Nae faith that
dug. Keep wearin that outfit n Toots'll be after ye: he's a man's
man as well!
    Aye well, Cherie grinned. Preachin to the converted then
int he?
    Ria wisnae making much sense – kept on drifting away n
then coming back, up to the eyeballs on the morphine. Cherie
couldnae sit still in there, uncomfy being with Ria without the
Saturday-night gear on. There was no lipstick n mascara to hide
behind. Didnae even feel like a Cherie on a miserable Tuesday
morning wi just the half day off work n needing to be back
before two. On Tuesday mornings she felt like she was just plain
old Stuart Hendry.
    At least Ria had the pharmaceuticals.
    Here, she says to Ria, Pass us over a couple of they grapes
willye?

Cherie's pal got sacked from the chemists shop n that was how
she met up wi Ria in the first place. Turns out they'd lived round
the corner fae each other for years n only knew each other's
faces from the clubs before then.
    Mad but, mental so it was. The pair of them both goin for
the same guy n bein that different n all that. Cherie always went
for they types – the big burly types, but Ria was more intae the
shaven-headed look. She liked guys that looked like they were
in the BNP n had a few run-ins when she played her cards

wrong n had to make a quick exit. Clackin along the Paisley Road outside after the Opry n stopping so's she could bend down n get the spike heels off.

Ya fuckin bent-shot! the skinhead was shouting. He caught up with Ria no bother, while she was trying to get the strap on the shoes undone. Then, she gets upn goes **WHACK** on the top of his head wi the heel.

OOYAH! the skinhead goes. **WHIT YE DAE THAT FOR?**

Aye – gauntae gie us a kickin are ye? Ria goes. Back tae my place if it's abuse ye want, ya wee fuckin acting-straight wee shitebag! Ye're as bent as me n ye know it! Ria stood there with all the folk spillin out the pubs looking to see what would happen next.

Nobody lifts a finger. Nobody moves a muscle.

Showdown time.

Ria had a gold-lame heel strap hooked round either thumb n her blond wig caught wee shimmers of smirr in it. Gold lamet dress n straw cowboy hat hanging back over her shoulder, tied with a pvc strap round her neck. The skinhead looked a bit shifty. His hand couldnae have moved more than a half-inch but Ria still beat him on the draw, both barrels blazing –

OOYAH! the Nazi goes. **WHIT YE DAE THAT FOR?**

Turns out he was only going to the sore bit on his nut where she chibbed him the first time.

Kick to kill, Ria doll! one of the other queens on the pavement shouts – the rest of them cheering n laughing. Ria twirls a shoe around her forefinger by the heel-strap then blows the smoke off the barrel n winks at them.

First thing Ria ever says to her was, Word of advice, doll – get riddae yir hairdresser. Cherie was totally mortified so she was. Dead close to the bone, Ria.

Her hair was all right but. It was they heels was the problem. Funny the things ye mind…

Cherie was seeing this guy on and off n she was dead intae him as well. She was wae Pin-the-Tail Tony in Safeways n he was asking her about the competition. Tony worked under Cherie in the chemist shop round the corner n was dead intae her too – but she was just blanking that.

NO, TONY, I'VE TOLD YE she says to him, n he's goin, Why no, Cherie, we've been seein each other for ages…?

Some guy so ye are, Tony, Cherie tells him. We've no *been*

seein each other. We're just good friends know what I mean? Sides I'm seein someone else, ye know that. I don't know why ye keep pesterin me about it...

Tony goes into a right huff about this. What's wrong wi him then? He not good enough for her or something?

Pin-the-Tail Tony man. Some banana so he was. Used to work on the railways – a signalman or something. One time he got called out with a bunch of the other guys cause there was something on the side of the track wanted shifting n Tony had to go all the way down there, out to Balloch or somewheres n it turned out to be a dead donkey. Nae wonder they'd no said why they wanted him. It was totally minging by the time they got there – ye could smell it about a half-mile away. It must have stuck its head through the fence at the side where the rail lines ran past the field it was in n got belted by the 12:30 inbound for Glasgow Central. By the time Tony got there the thing was totally hummin man. The middle of summer. All the guys stuck bits of hankie up their noses n took a leg a pair n got lifting. Tony got the back-right hoof n when they started trying to drag the thing the belly bursts open n all this melted gear comes pishing out. Wantin tae boak, Tony drops his left leg, stands on the tail n trips over it wi his right like it's an untied shoelace. Face first, right intae the thing. The belly of the beast.

Two of his mates have to lift him out, n they can hardly stand straight for laughing.

Mibby ye should keep the party games for the house, Tony, one of them says. They knew he was a great one for pinning tail n that...

It's cause I don't fancy ye, Tony – ye're too short, Cherie says to him.

Tony was about to say something about orthopaedic heels but Cherie butted in –

Sides the boy she was seein was hung like a fuckin horse! Cherie waved a courgette off the shelf in Tony's face. Tony backed away from it like he'd smelt a rotten egg.

Beat that if ye can! she says. Pin-the-Tail Tony's face was tripping him.

Ria says to the skinhead, What're ye havin? n he mumbles something about not wanting anything off her, his nut was too sore n what did she have to go and belt him for – he wisnae gaunnae do nothing so he wisnae.

Aw, on ye go, Adolf...just a wee one? Hmmm?

More mumbling n complaining but then the boy says:

My name's Gary.

There ye go, Gary! That'll kill ye or cure ye. Second thoughts – there isnae any cure for what you've got... Ria handed the boy a glass of something from out the kitchen. The skinhead eyed her.

What's that then?

Gary, Ria says, Ye *know* what it is sweetie...you're *queer*.

Gary took a sip of his drink:

I meant what's this I'm drinking!

Aaah! C'est le Jack Daniel's – the French way...

Gary just sat looking at the drink and swirling it round the glass so that the ice clinked about. He was dead young looking really. Mibby twenty-one or two. Lovely cheekbones but.

What's Jack Daniel's the French Way?

Quel idiot! Jacques Danielle's *est* le French way. Et Coca-Cola aussi... you do *like* it the French way, don't ye, Gary? Or are ye more inclined to Greek...no don't answer that...

Ria slipped down onto the couch beside him. Look at poor Gary-warry with the nasty lump on his head: here let Ria kiss it all better again. Ria slipped an arm around the back of Gary's neck and leaned over. Gary sort of sagged down into her chest, like all the air had been let out of him. Just then Toots came running in from the kitchen. He could get the door open if he just kept on pushing away at it with his front paws. He sat with one ear cocked, staring at the pair of them, now and then making these jealous wee whimpering noises.

Now now, Toots, Ria went. Don't be spoiling all mummy's fun... Away n look after Rodin...

Ye've got Rodan!? Gary says, jerking straight up again.

The actual actual model of Godzilla's arch-foe!? Fire Rodan, radioactive-ray-breathing pteranodon! Was it scale?

Eh, no, Ria says. Rodin's the cat. He's Toots' pal...you'll love him. He's a pure oil painting, honest.

Ria used to try to keep Gary on a tight leash, but it wisnae easy. Kept on gettin intae all sorts – no just the skinhead palaver. Once he was out that was him out in style. Nights it was clubbing n mad wi the Charlie n the pills. Days it was no gettin up for the job n trying to work out whose flat he was in, whose clothes these were n how was he gaunnae get back to Ria's.

Out on the tear again were we? Ria says opening the door. She had this look on her face that Gary couldnae take. He was always totally like, I'm sorry I'm sorry let us in please, Ria love, let us in please...

And she was always letting him back in. She didnae care what kind of states he was in, she was just wanting him back. She was still hopeful he might let her get her end away n if he was where she could keep an eye on him n feeling guilty then she was in with a good shout usually. She let him away n crash out in her bedroom. When he got up and showered n came through to the living room he wisnae so apologetic.

Go n sit in the kitchen while auntie Ria gets something tae eat for ye –

Auntie Ria can away tae fuck.

Now now – that's no way to talk in front of a lady is it?

Aye but there isnae any ladies here is there?

Ria was giving him the stare, but Gary parried it.

I cannae see any. Can you?

He kept on staring, chewing slowly on his bit of toasted bagel wi smoked salmon n cream cheese.

Naw. I cannae see any ladies about here.

Ria folded her arms n stared right back again.

Well tell us what it is that you *do* see, sweetheart.

Gary chewed the bagel.

I see Brendan Coyle: a past-it poof in a party frock.

Ria goes:

And I see Gary Sneddon...she paused a minute, then went: failed Hitler Youth, failed hard-man, failed all his O-Grades, and a failed cunt as well.

Gary Sneddon's mouth ground to a halt. His lips made a puckering shape. He sat totally still.

Tell me, Gary sweetheart – what's it like to be so *comprehensive* a failure?

Gary got up and walked out, grabbing his jacket n slinging it over one shoulder.

Ria had outdrew him again but she was wounded herself this time. Her trigger finger was getting rusty right enough. She sat with Toots on the couch in the evening, watching telly. They split a box of Ferrero Rocher between them n stuck Gary's copy of *Godzilla Versus The Smog Monster* in the video. Toots had to be the Ambassador again n was frankly sick of spoiling himself by the time the movie finished, but Ria had cheered up a bit n was ready for *Godzilla Versus King Ghidora*: one of the classics of the '70s neo-Godzilla series. Apparently.

Cherie chucked the bag onto the bed. Ria looked up. What's this? she says. She was deteriorating fast. A slow pneumonia in the lungs.

Grapes, Cherie says.

Christ...I've grapes coming out ma arse in this place...

Ye can get creams for that, ye know. One needn't suffer in silence any longer. It's time to come out, sweetie.

Ria smiled. She looked terrible.

Gary in with you? Ria says, a hopeful look lurking about her face.

Cherie went, Naw, n looked at the bag on the bedspread. Not mind I told ye he disnae see me? He'll have got himself some other old trout by now.

That other guy, what about him?

Who?

Your sidekick – the short one with the orthopaedic shoes...

Tony?

Aye.

Don't ask, Ria. Don't even ask. She plucked a grape off the vine in the brown poke n popped it into her gub: Gie's a haemorrhoid then, she says. Ria's eyes wobbled round the room, then closed. She let out a gurgling sigh that sounded like her lungs were full of snotter.

Do us a favour, she went, keeping her eyes shut. Take some money from my account n get me a new dressing-gown n some make-up. I want to look my best...

Cherie chewed her grape, saying nothing.

The card's in my purse in the cabinet, Ria says, I'll give you the PIN.

That Tony's a pure maddie, Cherie told Ria. But sort of predictable as well. The time he crashed at her bit after the party. Cherie woke up in a total state, on the couch, everybody gone. The stereo still playing, ashtrays n bottles everywhere.

Ria coughed a lump of brown matter.

I was dying of thirst, Cherie says. I got up n went to the kitchen for a glass off water n my heid was nippin me...

Mines is nippin me the now, Ria says. You're the heidnip.

...and on the middle of the floor, on the lino was – guess what?

I don't know. What?

An empty whisky bottle, an uncooked pie wi a single bite out it and –

And what?

A coil of shite.

A what? Ria says. A coil of shite?

A coil of *human* shite, Cherie nodded.

So what happened? Ria went.

So I went to try the bedroom – I knew fine well he'd have curled up in there hoping I'd climb in beside him, the dirty stopover. The door was locked but. So I hammers on the door: !!!!!!!!TONY, I goes. **TONY!!!!!!!! WHERE THE FUCKTHAT PIE COME FAE!!!!????**

Ria snorted so hard that stuff came out her nose.

Tony lost his job in the chemist shop the same day Gary Sneddon came in. Tony knew it was him Cherie was seeing. The skinny wee Nazi prick had let himself get picked up by her at some nightclub or other, some tranny night, somewhere all they old queens could stand about n pose while the young meat dangled the carrot in front of them. That Gary fucker was one of the ones doing the dangling. Tony knew his face. Cherie near came to blows wi some other old slapper over him – some old trout wi a blond wig n heels. Cherie telt all this to Tony while they tramped round Safeways n he knew he had no chance now, he'd been kidding himself on about Cherie n him all the time. Cherie even showed him a picture the pair of them had taken in a photo-booth, Cherie on the bastard's lap, pouting n planting his cheek wi scarlet lipstick.

So there was her n this boy thegither at the bar having a drink when this blonde bitch wi a lame dress n spike heels turns up. Total nightmare so it was. Some tongue she had on her as well.

Tony says nothing.

Ye listening to me, Tony? Cherie goes. Tony was footering wi a packet of condoms or something. He had something else in his hand as well.

What the fuck ye doin? Cherie yelled at him. Tony sat there, the packet of condoms in one hand n the sewing needle from one of the first-aid kits in the other.

I mean what the fuck do ye think ye're doing?

She grabbed the wee packet out his hand n emptied it into her palm. She turned it over, examining the foil wrapper, holding it up to the light and squinting at it. One one side of the wrapper, in the centre of the condom, was a single, barely visible hole.

How long's this been goin on for?! Many've these ye put back on the shelves!?

She grabbed Tony by the hair and shook him back and forth, slicing the flat of her hand against his cheek, clawing him so that he had to hunch into a ball before the other sales assistants dragged her off.

GET OUT OF HERE NOW, YE HEAR ME! GET OUT, YA SICK FUCK!

Tony was already halfway out the door, checking for blood on his face with the palm of his hand. Fucking cow, he was saying to himself, his hand shaking. He felt sick. He was bleeding from the cheek. She had opened up his face. Fucking-fucking-fucking cow, he was saying. Fucking-dirty-fucking-past-it-fuckin-tranny-bitch-fucking-**COW**! He would have to find somewhere – a public lavatory or something – n get it cleaned up. He didnae want to risk an infection setting in. He held a paper hankie to his cheek and stumbled off up the road.

It was weird how Cherie n Ria only got friendly after Ria got sick. They were aye at each other's throats before that. The Gary Sneddon business. Ria had left a message on Cherie's ansafone after forcing Gary to gie her the number n then Gary disappeared, no able to handle it. Ria reckoned he'd headed for Manchester. Plenty more auld queens down that neck of the woods.

How did ye get him to give ye it? Cherie went. She could never get Gary to do anything once he'd set his mind to it.

I telt him I'd hidden his Godzilla videos. And I was gaunnae burn them less he gave us it.

Christ I hate Godzilla, Cherie went.

But ye like Rodan, don't ye?

Oh aye. Rodin's fine.

Thing is, Ria says, Gary still reckons he isnae queer. In denial or what? Apparently, we never even did it... he wisnae there when it didn't happen. Silly boy...

Great cheekbones but, Cherie went.

Mmm, Ria went. Absolutely...

How d'ye like the dressing-gown anyway? Not too showy?

Showy? Ye kiddin? It's me ye're talking to, honey!

Aye well.

The thing was, they never really mentioned it – no after Cherie came up negative n stayed that way. They never mentioned who gave what to who. It stopped being important. Even Gary Sneddon stopped being important. There was other stuff to think about.

So, Cherie went. Why is Rodin called Rodin anyway?

Ria paused for a second, spitting grape seeds into her palm.

Same reason Godzilla's called Godzilla I suppose, she said, n popped another grape into her mouth.

So, Ria says. Ye tellin us what happened wi Tony or not?

Gaunnae no ask me that, Ria, Cherie went.

How?

They both grinned, enjoying the joke while it lasted.

Jist... gaunnae no?

Paul Brownsey

PUBLIC FIGURES

There is a woman in the West End of Glasgow who spends her life seeing inside other people's homes. Morning, afternoon, evening – she's available to view your home at all hours. She gets to do her rubbernecking via the estate agents and the property columns in the newspapers. Of course, the estate agents have got her number, but short of a blunt refusal, what can they do when she requests viewing details? Often they drop a hint to you: '…and there's a Mrs MacAndrew at 6.15. However, she has been viewing a *lot* of properties lately and we *wouldn't* be *very* confident of a sale, on *this* occasion.'

She hasn't the slightest intention of buying any of the houses she views. And it's not that she wants to see inside this or that *particular* home, as you or I might quite like to look around that flat in Belhaven Terrace with the gorgeous ice-blue wedding-cake ceiling and the fireplace supposed to have been designed by one of Mackintosh's brothers; or as we might have a sneaking fancy to see the domestic setting of those notorious marital dramas of the Dows down the street. That would just be normal curiosity. But Mrs MacAndrew is indiscriminate: any home will do to feed her gaze, yours, mine, anybody's.

Pathetic, really. There must be a terrible vacuum inside her, driving her to this relentless hungry visual absorption of other people's homes. And not just their homes, of course. People's homes reflect their – what? – their inner fibre and desire and being, and that's what she's trying to capture because she's so lacking in substance herself. Naturally, her attempt is doomed to fail, for if you are hollow the remedy is not to feed off other people but to – well, the phrase says it all: 'Get a life!'

She didn't *seem* pathetic when she arrived at our flat, I'll grant her that. Her rather gentle voice over the entry 'phone exactly hit the mark between apology for intrusion and confidence in having legitimate business. Well, she'd had enough practice.

She was fiftyish, not quite motherly but somehow willing to be if required. Her dark curly hair was a neat mop. Her large eyes were not timid, exactly; rather, expression was in abeyance as though she hadn't yet received instructions as to what response to make. She stood there in her belted grey raincoat and knee-length boots, her hands crossed comfortably in front of her, and she looked patiently at *me*, not at the flat.

'This is what they call the dining-hall. Entrance-hall and dining-room combined.'

Only then did her eyes leave me and begin to travel the room; she stayed rooted at the door. Our dining-table was a bit too small for the room, but that ought not to matter to a purchaser. The fact that the maroon carpeting extended eighteen inches *up* the walls might matter to a purchaser, but then, Mrs MacAndrew wasn't in business to purchase.

There was a flash. She had taken an instant camera from her black leather shoulder-bag and had used it. Prospective purchasers do sometimes take pictures these days, but this was without so much as a by-your-leave, and I was sarcastic.

'Is this a photo-shoot for *Hello!* magazine?'

'So you like *Hello!* too.' Congratulating me. 'You can learn so much from famous people, can't you? Doris Day, now, such a genuine person, I read somewhere that she lives all by herself with some dogs and says they're her best friends. I've got two dogs and they're *my* best friends, too, since my divorce.' She said 'my divorce' as if it were a badge of admission to the VIP lounge. 'When my husband left me I was a broken woman. Like Paul Gascoigne was a broken man when his wife left him, I read it.'

Then she spoke with the obliging delight with which parents examine something the child has made at school and brought home to show them: 'Now this looks like a home in which people have been happy!'

No, we hadn't been. That was why we were selling: we were splitting up. We had never been anything but two lonely people pretending we were in love. But that was none of her business.

'We're leaving the carpets.'

Her eyes were on the carpeting going up the walls, above the skirting-board. 'Yes, that *does* work,' she murmured, more to herself than to me. Brightly: 'It gives *such* a sense of warmth and generosity.'

I was annoyed at myself for feeling pleased by the approval of someone like her. True, she'd seen inside enough houses.

I remembered the day we had chosen the carpet, driving round to various carpet warehouses, bringing a certain some-thing into the assistants' faces and voices as we explained our idea: 'Up the *wall*? I see.' And it had been that evening that we'd met Kodaly's great-nephew at a party given by someone who worked in admin for one of the city's orchestras. I don't think either of us had ever heard a note of Kodaly but we kept a conversation going with him, and afterwards we felt such frauds because apparently he'd remarked on our intelligent conversation.

In the 'galley' kitchen Mrs MacAndrew's eyes widened as though forced to do so by the pressure of the approval that flooded into them. 'Oh yes!'

I was provoked to point out that because the kitchen was long and narrow, you were forever getting in each other's way if you were both trying to do things in there at the same time. This could do no harm, for she had no intention of buying.

'Yes, I can see it all. Colliding and dropping things and having to clear up messes.' She sighed fondly at the vision.

Her eyes roamed, not so much over the fixtures and fittings, I thought, as over the personal, transient things: the packet of oatmeal, which we both preferred to rolled oats for porridge (well, you're supposed to have shared interests, aren't you?), the bottle of 'environmental' washing-up liquid I'd bought.

'No good on grease, is it?' she said.

'Perhaps not.' Barely polite, no more.

'I *admire* people who will make a sacrifice for things that are important.'

That didn't sound like me at all. It had just been a Pavlov's-dogs reaction to the word 'environmental' on the label.

Indignantly I talked about fuel bills, but her avid eyes had ascended to the drying-rack suspended from the ceiling and were rewarded by tee-shirts belonging to both of us, all a bit purplishly discoloured because the red-and-blue-striped jogging socks I'd once put in to wash with them had run. We'd had a hell of a row about that in the foyer of the Glasgow Film Theatre, where we'd gone to see a revival of *Madame Bovary*, and the row had made me feel absolutely laid waste and empty.

She was scrutinising the bathroom when I told her the entry date. At once she fixed me with a look of concern. 'As soon as that?' She might have been a serious buyer and this a problem for her. My annoyance with Mrs MacAndrew spilled over and I decided to let her have it.

'We'd be happy to negotiate with anyone who wasn't a time-waster. But since we are splitting up, it seemed a good idea not to prolong the agony and to get out as soon as possible. We are – have been – a gay couple.' The woman at the estate agent's, smiling like someone bringing us good news, had said there was no need to mention that, and that we still had lots of selling points. Under 'Vendor' on the schedule for the public they put Richard's name only.

'Oh, the end of a dream! Like the Prince and Princess of Wales.'

Clearly, the end of our dream gave new meaning to the suite from B&Q and the towels from Habitat. Her eyes went over the bathroom a second time, then they gazed into mine as if a video drama-doc of our tragedy was playing in them. 'I can see the two of you in this flat, loving each other, trying so hard to build a happy future together. Like Elton John and his partner, I saw them on television, you could see they really love each other, it was at Diana's funeral. Ah, she somehow made every-one's compassion just that bit more real, didn't she?'

Her eyes enveloped me with her own compassion. 'But it all went wrong for you.'

I brooded on the phrase 'went wrong'. It implied rich potential stymied, two people with full souls and full stature embarking on a venture that promised happiness and that failed almost unaccountably, from some accident. That was precisely how things had *not* been. It had been a thin, clutching business; we had been too *needy*.

In the lounge or sitting-room – we had never fixed on a designation and I suppose that symbolised the void at the centre of us – she said, 'Lovely, lovely,' and her face had the entranced look of someone with their nose pressed to a window gazing in on scenes of joy and fulfilment. Well, there had certainly been scenes.

She touched the settee, reverently, and I admonished her: 'We're not leaving the suite.' We had got it through Richard's brother, who is deputy manager of a furniture warehouse on the South Side of the city. He was the only member of Richard's family I'd met; his mother had said that of course he was still a member of the family but his private life had to be kept to him-self. The brother had offered us the suite for nothing, saying he could enter it as damaged goods, but Richard and I – we had agreed on this, and the discovery had been a brief moment of pleasure – had said we wouldn't take it at all unless we could pay the normal employee-discount price.

'Of course, he'll pocket it all and still put it down as wast-age,' Richard added.

'In that case, why did he offer it to us for free in the first place?' Richard's remark had been so *stupid*; what's more, if he was so set on bad-mouthing his own brother for no reason, how might he not talk about me?

In the narrow part of the hall, from which the bedrooms led off, I rapped the wall and gave Mrs MacAndrew my usual spiel: 'There's supposed to be a room there between the bedrooms that was bricked over when the big house was converted into flats.' I explained that if you measured the rooms against the length of the hall, they fell short by about eight feet.

She rapped it, too. 'It *does* sound hollow. A secret room!' Excitedly.

'Perhaps a dressing-room. Or perhaps the landing for a second staircase, for servants perhaps, and it was just simpler to brick it up rather than remove it. That's what Richard thinks. My ex-partner.'

'Why don't you open it up?' A jolly-wheeze voice.

'We're moving.' Drily.

'You never know what you might find.'

'A corpse, perhaps.' The corpse of our relationship? Irrelevantly I pictured a corpse at a dressing-table, powder-puff in hand, death-grin features recognisable as Mrs MacAndrew's. I said cheekily, 'That could be something for you to do if you buy the flat.'

'Oh, you two try it!' Indulge yourselves, have another chocolate. 'I can just see you and your lover working away together among the bricks and dust, making something of it.'

The picture she communicated to me went unexamined beneath my astonishment at Mrs MacAndrew's unforced use of the word 'lover'. It couldn't have been her natural mode of expression, yet there was no sense of the ironic inverted commas with which it needed to be surrounded on account of its suggesting a sort of passionate grandeur that had been so conspicuously absent from our puny little experiment in connection.

I said, 'Perhaps *Hello!* would like to come and do a photo-shoot of us at work.'

Her face lit up as at a real possibility.

She winced when I spoke of viewing the bedrooms and pointedly put her camera away. She looked at mine with a pained tragic frown on her face like she'd just been told that this was the very room in which Richard Burton and Elizabeth

Taylor called it a day and they had been very dear friends of hers. My Richard's, well, not *my* Richard's, Richard's, obviously no spare bedroom, she didn't enter at all. She stood at the threshold, bending forward and swivelling her body in a brief token of inspection but with a brave blasted look like someone having formally to identify a loved one's body.

'The separation.' Whispered, eyes down, as befitted a tragedy.

'Actually, there never was anything but separation.'

I had had enough of her ghastly vampire-like craving to fill herself with the blood of others' lives. It was time to put an end to this.

'Well now, will you be wanting a survey done?'

'I *do* have other properties to view.'

'I bet you do.' Letting her know I knew.

'It's a *very* nice flat and in many ways it would suit me *very* well. But...'

Her look coyly requested permission to speak. I was stony-faced and silent.

'I can see the two of you regretting the loss of your lovely home, saying, "Why, oh why, did we let that woman have it?" You see, people do start over.' Presuming I'd know the phrase. 'John Lennon and Yoko Ono did. Myself, I think Nelson Mandela would have liked to with Winnie.'

'If you're suggesting a survey would be wasted, I can assure you it would not be.'

As she left she looked ashamed of herself.

When Richard came in from his chess club I said, 'That Mrs MacAndrew came to view. You know, the woman who spends her life seeing inside other people's homes.'

'We must be genuine members of the human race. At least, the part of it that sells houses. Something to tell our grand-children about.' His usual self-absorbed way of talking, eyes focused inwards, as though speaking for his own ears only. He said, 'What was she like?' but there was no curiosity in it: he had found the question in a checklist of things you say by way of conversation.

I followed him into the kitchen. He put the kettle on, milk into one tea-cup. 'Ordinary-looking. A nutter. Husband left her. No wonder. Absolutely non-existent self-esteem, so she creeps around thinking other people's lives are grand and dramatic. For instance, she seems to think we're in the Charles and Diana class when it comes to the End Of A Dream.' Capitals to signify heavy irony. 'And she thought the carpet going up the walls *wasn't* naff, arbiter of taste that she is. I'm a worthwhile person for buying environmental washing-up liquid. And she urges us to open up the secret room and has a fantasy of us in hard hats sawing timbers and chiselling away at bricks.'

'Actually, it would be me doing the sawing and chiselling, your contribution being to read out the relevant bits of the *Reader's Digest Manual of Beautiful Homes*.' Wit for his own entertainment, not even to wound.

He stood holding the carton of milk and his mouth gave an irritated twitch that said he couldn't return it to the fridge because I was blocking the way.

I moved the wrong way, we collided, milk slopped out of the packet, spattered onto the floor.

'I told her about that, how crowded it gets in here. She said she could see it all. Colliding and dropping things and having to clear up messes. All part of a tremendously enviable life-style, she seemed to think.'

'Not a bad idea, though.' Milk back in the fridge, he crouched to wipe up the mess. 'Opening up the secret room. Could be a utility room or child's bedroom. An extra Selling Point.' Capitals for irony again. As he squeezed the cloth under the tap his eyes sought mine.

'So,' he said, in a voice that didn't so much sketch a hypo-thetical course of action as spell out something already decided, which was so like him, not treating me as an equal partner in a decision, 'we take the house off the market and get to work.'

I had an odd impulse to tell this to Mrs MacAndrew, but I had no 'phone number for her and it wasn't something you could ask the estate agent's to pass on to her.

Tom Bryan

DIASPORA

I've met them in New York
Toronto and Detroit.
Janitors, night watchmen
working or seeking work.

Stooped in graveyard shift
thermos and lunch pail,
feeding dreams of Clisham
or the North Minch drift.

These men and women were never bought,
wore their dignity like well-washed tweed.
Kept songs and stories deep within –
withheld gently from the melting pot.

Leanne Bunce

WESTERN CHARM

red deserts

Wild sage
grows on red

of New Mexico.

Native American

From ancient
ruins

plains

I   absorb   these

rocks

and   distant

mountains.

not   yet

I am a tourist.
My friend and I
wave at our shadows.
We laugh;
our silhouettes look
like aliens.

I have heard
burning sage
will ward off evil.
I steal some
to take the desert

home.

Larry Butler

THE STORY

1. Hello ... Yes ... No ... in the Botanics?! ... No! ... really!
... in the middle of the day! ... I would have screamed ... Why
did you stop? ... You didn't ... Did he touch you? ... How big
was it? ... My God! ... a cleaver ... really! ... Oh how could
you, I could've never done that ... you certainly were lucky ...
I would've given it to him straight away ... was he Scottish? ...
Glaswegian? ... couldn't you tell? ... ok I'll meet you at the
metro at half past two.

•

2. I'm walking down the steps by Kelvin Way. down. down.
down them steps with rain dripping off bare branches thudding
on my brollie. Thud. Thud. Thud. On the bridge, you ask me
the time: 'Have ya got the time, miss?' On the white bridge you
ask me the time. I hear the ducks: quack quack quack. I hear
the robin. '1:36' I say – you look lost – I think. Black eye, short-
cropped hair, pink anorak, early twenties, lost, you look lost.
I'm on my way to the bank to pay in one hundred and fifty
pounds cash – in an envelope – in my rucksack – I don't believe
it – in my rucksack, in my rucksack is one hundred and fifty
pounds cash. Over the bridge I turn round. You wave and say:
'Is this the Botanics ... which way do I go?' You walk towards
me. I pause. pause. pause. You are lost I think you are lost. lost.
lost. Quite close now – a metre away – you reveal from under
your coat a kitchen knife, a cleaver. cleaver. cleaver. 'Gimme yr
bag' you say in a quiet faltering voice while gesturing towards
me with the knife. You look left right left right left right. Your
eyes wander like a frightened squirrel. I step back. 'Don't move'
you say. 'Don't be silly' I say. 'Don't do this, I'm not going to
give you may bag.' my bag. my bag. He says: 'You're lucky this
time.' He turns and runs runs runs up the steps to Botanic
Crescent. I run run run up the steps – pink anorak – into the
gardens – short cropped hair – as another man walks down the
steps deep in his own thoughts oblivious of my situation. I
phone the police from a shop in Byres Rd.

•

3. 'Tell me what happened.' I walked down the steps to the river, as I crossed the white bridge into the Botanics, a man asked me the time. 'What was the time?' 1:36. He looked lost. 'What did he look like? Describe him.' A black eye, short hair – dirty blond – dark pink anorak, dark with rain. After crossing the bridge I turned to look at him. He waved to me. I walked towards him. He walked towards me. When he got close he asked me if this was the Botanic Gardens. Then he pulled a knife. 'Which hand?' Left hand. 'What kind of knife?' A square kitchen knife – a cleaver. 'Did he threaten you?' He held it close to his side and just kept saying 'gimme yr bag, gimme yr bag' while pushing the knife towards me. He looked left and right and behind, his eyes wandering like a frightened animal. I stepped back. 'Don't move' he said. 'Don't be silly, don't do this. I'm not going to give you my bag...' I said. I felt stronger than him. He was nervous, not sure of himself. 'Yr lucky this time,' he said as he turned and ran over the bridge and up the steps to Botanic Crescent. I don't remember what sort of trousers, I didn't notice his shoes. Smaller than me. Black eye. Square kitchen knife. 'Scottish', yes Scottish. 'Glaswegian?' yes Glaswegian accent. I phoned the police from a shop in Byres Road.

•

4. I will walk down the steps to the River Kelvin. On the bridge to the Botanics, a man will ask me the time. He will have a black eye and look a bit lost. As I look at my watch – 1:36 – it will fall off my wrist into the river. That's all I remember.

Ron Butlin

UNDER AFRICAN SKIES

Mary has always known the meaning of *good*: if a black was disrespectful, her father used to beat him with one of his hand-made whips while everyone in the small leatherwork factory and household, including her, was assembled to look on. One particularly hot afternoon he'd been in the middle of carrying out a punishment for lateness when, with his arm raised to full stretch, he had screamed, dropped his whip and fallen facedown in the dirt. By the end of the following day he had been laid to rest; by the end of the following week the factory was closed. Even though she had recently turned forty, Mary insisted she would remain to run the Mission; and so it was over ten years until she followed her mother back to Scotland. By now, the old woman needed looking after.

It was early November. Caring for her mother and getting to know the people in the village was pleasant enough, except when they asked about 'conditions' in the new South Africa or, as she preferred to call it, the *race situation*. At first, she offered to tell them about the small clinic where she'd taught hygiene and contraception, bandaged sores and given vaccinations. She soon learned to save her breath. The would-be idealists wanted something to be angry at, that was all, and the opportunity to demonstrate a worldly wisdom for which there was no scope in their wet grey little Scottish village.

A month after arriving, she'd met Mrs Collingwood at a Christmas Sale of Work and been invited to call. She was nervous as she turned off the road and walked in through the gateless entrance: the pair of six-foot-high pillars marked the only gap in the massive stone wall around the grounds. Purple and red rhododendron bushes lined the gravel path, between the bare branches of oak and beech she could see tall chimneys set in a sea of slates; she passed an archway leading to a cobbled courtyard, stables and outbuildings; the tennis court had a permanently off-season feel with its rotted posts, weeds and no net. The Collingwoods, so she'd been told by the woman who'd introduced them, had lived in Zimbabwe before selling up their farm a few years back. Evidently, they'd got out just in time. As she walked up to the large sandstone house Mary reminded herself that here, at least, there should be no *difficult* questions.

The moment she was shown into the bay-windowed sitting-room she knew she had done right in accepting the older woman's invitation. The set of carved masks that hung along one wall and the ebony figurines clustered here and there on the bookshelves and mantelpiece all seemed to be greeting her warmly; and Mrs Collingwood herself was clearly pleased to see her again:

'I'm so glad you could come – we're sure to have lots to chat about together. You were in South Africa, I believe.'

As she told her mother later, the afternoon simply flew past. They talked about the African countryside, the hot sun, the abruptness of day and night, the wildlife, the Mission, her father's factory, the Collingwoods' farm. They had tea, some cakes. After Mary brought out her photographs, Mrs Collingwood produced hers. It was nearly five when they parted.

'You must come again soon, Mary. It's so good to chat with someone who really understands what you're talking about.'

The two women smiled at each other.

Around nine that evening, having helped her mother upstairs to the bathroom, Mary saw to her needs, washed her, dried her then put her to bed. She switched off the electric blanket and made sure the red emergency call-button was within reach. It was when Mary was bending over to give the goodnight kiss and customary, 'Sleep well, Mother,' that the old woman grabbed her shoulder and hissed loudly,

'Your father is a good man.' The unblinking eyes stared into hers: '*Good* – do you understand?'

'Good? Of course.'

'You must never forget that.'

'I won't, Mother.'

'So we must be sure to tell him.'

'In our prayers?'

'You can tell him to his face, can't you?'

'To his face? ... Mother?'

With a sigh the old woman lay back down on the bed. 'When he comes in from the workshop – be sure to go to him and tell him. Don't wait. There's a good girl.'

*

Next morning, as usual, they had breakfast together in the glassed-over rear porch her mother called the *conservatory*. Layer upon layer of black cloud seemed only just inches above them, heavy rain drummed loudly onto the panes; through the streaming glass the garden had a sodden underwater look. Against this shifting backdrop her mother's movements – the awkward lifting and replacing of a cup, her clumsy bites at a piece of toast – were turned into puppet-like jerks of spoiled coordination as if the water, or some crueller element, had already got into the works.

From time to time, while writing a thank-you note to Colly, using the nickname her new acquaintance had insisted upon, Mary leant over to wipe dribbles from the slackened mouth across the table. All at once the old woman jerked her head free:

'My daughter's in Africa, you know.'

'Yes, Mother, I was there for nearly —'

'My daughter is in Africa, in South Africa to be precise.'

Mary pretended she hadn't heard. 'Would you like me to turn up the fire a little?'

There was no response.

Breakfast over, the old woman sat back, stretched out her hands and started picking at the loose skin. Nearly a minute passed, then she let them drop onto her lap.

'Mary takes care of the natives, you know. Takes good care of them. She's a saint. I keep all her letters. I must show them to you sometime.' Then a glance and a smile, 'Yes, you're right, it *is* rather cold. Another bar would be a kindness.'

After crouching to reset the switch, Mary got to her feet and, without meaning to, found herself staring down at her mother's trembling hands, at their criss-cross of discoloured markings and veins. It reminded her of a nest she'd been shown once out in the bush: coil upon seething coil of black and vermilion snakes. Abruptly, she cleared the small table and went to wash the dishes. The old woman gave no sign of noticing her leave the room but sat staring out at the down-pour, saying nothing.

It rained most of the weekend. Sunday morning began with a few patches of blue sky, a watery blue that soon darkened to daylong twilight. The two women watched TV, ate their meals and at about eight o'clock Mary helped her mother upstairs.

She was getting her settled when the old woman sat up, her

face radiant as she pointed to the foot of the bed:

'Look! Look! Isn't it beautiful!'

Mary looked, but could see nothing.

'So beautiful! So beautiful!' she kept repeating, almost ecstatic, her hands straining forwards: 'The sun! The sun! Let me touch. Please, please let me touch!'

'You should lie down, Mother. It's time to sleep. Come on.'

Mary did her best to ease her back down, all the while saying, 'Time to sleep, Mother. We'll get you comfortable.'

'But I want to touch the sun. It's there. Let me touch it. Please, please.' She began to sob.

A moment later she seemed to have lost interest and had slumped back against the pillows.

Mary straightened the covers: 'Feeling better now, Mother? I'll leave the night-light on, and the bell's there if you need me. Sleep well.'

The old woman gazed up at her: 'My usual nanny's black, who are you?'

'But, Mother...'

'*You*'re not my mother. I know you're not.' Then she turned her face away and pretended to go to sleep.

*

The weather lifted slightly on Monday, but it wasn't until late on Tuesday that Colly phoned to thank her for the card and suggest she drop by again soon – how did Friday afternoon suit?

Three whole days, thought Mary, as she put down the phone.

Once again they were in the African Room, as Mary called it to herself: her hostess in the large armchair by the fire, and her on the couch. The sherry that Colly had poured was already making her feel light-headed and, after a few minutes, Mary found herself talking about her mother. She could feel the beginnings of tears pricking behind her eyes.

'Must be very hard,' Colly was saying, 'I doubt if I could cope... Take the patience of a saint, I'd imagine.'

Mary took another sip of sherry, her head swam pleasantly. 'I do what I can, that's all.'

'Always have, it seems. Looking after the people at your

mission, and now your mother. What about you?'

'Me?' She laughed, she was deliciously dizzy now. 'What about me?'

'Well, if you don't mind my asking, who's ever looked after *you*?'

The pleasant dizziness just seemed to be going on and on.

'My mother's always done what she thought right.'

Not quite what she meant to say, but it didn't seem to matter.

Could it be the heat from the fire that was making her cheeks flush? She sank back into the couch, into the relaxing smell of the leather. So familiar, like one of those hot days when she'd sit in the veranda shade and there'd be the freshly tanned skins stacked in bundles waiting for the lorry to take them to the rail depot for Jo'burg. When she let her eyes close, she could easily imagine herself still under the clear blue skies of Africa.

Next moment, she was aware that Colly had reached over and was giving her hand a squeeze.

When it was time to leave, her coat just *wouldn't* seem to go on. She felt a proper fool standing there in the hall, her arm jammed halfway down one sleeve while she struggled with the other. Colly had started to laugh:

'Mary, I'm sorry but – that's actually *my* coat you're trying on.'

'Oh! Excuse me! Please excuse me!'

'An easy mistake – nearly the same colour.'

How could she have got them mixed up? Colly was being kind, of course. She'd just panicked.

'Allow me, madam' – the older woman was holding her coat for her, pretending to be an attendant.

'Thank you.' Mary trembled as she put first one arm into its sleeve, then the other. A perfect fit.

'You must be sure to come again, madam. You look splendid now.'

'Thank you, I'm sorry to have made such a terrible mistake. So *embarrassing*.' She was aware of her hostess behind her, straightening the lie of the collar on her shoulders.

'I'd have got the best of the bargain! Anyway, Mary, that's what friends are for – when I was a girl we were always swapping clothes for those nights out that were going to change our lives!'

'Yes, I suppose...'

'Don't think about it.' Colly opened the front door and added, in a more serious tone of voice, 'I hope we become friends.'

'Yes, that would be...' she hesitated, not sure exactly what she wanted to say. 'That would be...good,' she added, then turned to glance outside: 'At least it's not raining any more.'

Having said goodbye she hurried off down the drive.

*

Mary knew her mother never allowed alcohol in the house, not even the cider vinegar which might have helped her rheumatism, and so, on arriving home she wasn't surprised when the old woman made a great show of sniffing the air disapprovingly. This censorious reserve, maintained for the first quarter of an hour, was more than made up for during their evening meal by her mother talking on and on about Mary, her wonderful daughter in South Africa. Mary this, Mary that, and Mary everything. How thoughtful Mary was, how kind Mary was, how good Mary was. Had Mary wanted, she could have been married a dozen times over. Mary was such a thoughtful girl, such a caring girl. Mary had chosen a life of selfless dedication. Grandchildren would have been nice, of course, but still...

'Her father can tell you all about her mission work, if you didn't mind waiting a moment.' She added, 'He'll be back shortly, he's out in the yard teaching some blacks a lesson in respect. Can't you hear?'

'Hear what, Mother?'

The old woman edged a little forward in her chair: there was a faint knowing smile and a flinch: '*That*...and *that*. He knows he has a duty, a responsibility...'

Two hours later as she was helping her mother upstairs the old woman suddenly pushed her away shouting, 'Who *are* you? Who are you? Where's Mary, where's my daughter Mary? Leave me alone.' Pausing halfway up the stairs to gaze blankly around her, she called out, 'Mary! Mary!'

They carried on, step after step, until almost at the top, her mother pushed her away again. This time with such force that Mary stumbled, both hands grabbing for the banister rail.

Having steadied herself she turned and was just in time to see her mother staggering to regain her balance, and failing.

And screaming. As if it was happening in slow-motion, she watched the old woman claw at the empty air, then go tumbling down the entire flight of stairs hitting her head against the banister, against the wall.

Seconds later she lay at the bottom, a smashed huddle. She was moaning. Still alive. Mary knew better than to move her.

This morning, Mary's brought herself some breakfast through on a tray to the conservatory. She knows she can't afford to linger, there's a great deal to be done today – phonecalls to make, letters to write, her mother's papers to sort through. As she sips her first cup she senses a weight of guilt threatening to descend on her, and crush her. Facts must be faced, she tells herself: she *panicked*. What other explanation can there be? Doctor Ross had been furious with her. While grabbing his bag he'd yelled at her: didn't she understand that delay could mean the difference between life and death? Coming all the way over to the surgery, for God's sake – why hadn't just she phoned him? She'd started to cry and kept trying to explain how quickly it had all happened, how sorry she was, how she'd had no time to think even. She'd been so confused. There'd not been a phone at the Mission, that was all. As he hustled her out to his car she couldn't seem to stop saying, 'We hadn't a phone at the Mission. We hadn't a phone.'

That had been twelve hours ago. Realising she's on the verge of tears again, she's begun repeating the very same phrases, this time to the empty porch: 'I just didn't think! I just didn't stop to think!' As if pleading to the dark clouds she can see through the smeared glass above her, she says the words over and over: 'There was no phone at the Mission. No phone.' She's shaking her head for emphasis, 'It's true. It's *true*.'

When the doorbell rings she gets to her feet.

On her way to answer it, she catches sight of her reflection in the hall mirror. She pauses. The beginnings of vanity? She almost smiles at the thought. Then bites her lip, hard. For several seconds she stares at the neatly brushed hair, the saddened eyes, the tremble in the corner of her mouth. She knows that nowhere else will she find the reassurance she needs and longs for. Nor any hope of absolution.

The doorbell rings again, and she goes to greet whoever's there.

Ken Campbell

THE GURNIE

You could always draw good crack from the Gurnie. He'd talk of trees and burns, and birds and keepers and march the old estates and say what farm was held by whom and who had it before and mind the ruined cottage by the stank and name the great-grandchildren now at the school who couldna mind auld Erchie and didna ken that the love that bred them had its ghosts among the nettles by the crumbling walls.

I mind once tracing with him the lie of the land round Cruachan. He had been there when they put the Hydro scheme in and he explained in great detail how it was done. For fully thirty minutes I understood, with unsung clarity, the balanced pressures and grid sunk drying concrete and how the shuttering was central to the whole. It escaped me soon, that knowledge, but it never left him and he could convey it with a clarity that even now can penetrate my fuddled brain.

And there was Foxie who had driven all the roads. We'd trace the routes to Mull or Islay and hear of jobs long forgot and dams put in, the roads improved and bridges and bothie huts and farms kent to them both.

'You mind yon woman that had Killauchtie? You'll ken her. Her that had the three sons.'

'That had the land that ran down to the shore? Where the boat came in?'

'Aye, that's her. That kept losing sheep with every high winter spring.'

'Yon were three braw laddies though.'

'Ach they couldnae manage a whippet. She'd yin guid dug but the boys had nae idea.'

'Kelpie, that was its name.'

'Aye, Kelpie. Ye never saw a better dog than Kelpie. Oh she could handle yon and keep the yowes awa frae the bottom end o the park. But ach the boys spoilt all the others.'

'What became of them?'

'They say the eldest went into the law.'

Embarrassed they looked at me and I grinned. 'That would finish it then.'

'Aye,' said Foxie. 'That feenisht it. T'ither twa was college boys. Yin til teaching, t'ither – I dinna ken. Management or some siclike.'

'And herself?' asked the Gurnie.

'Wha's to ken. The land's sold. Some English or ither's got it and putting chalets up a' around the bay.'

The Gurnie chuckled. 'Yin guid sou'westerly – that'll sort it.'

We sat, still for a moment, gazing into our pints. Davie was at the other end of the bar.

'Naw, he was in here last night. He seemed fine enough to me anyway.' And turning to wash glasses in the new machine Peter had installed, catching my eye and nodding.

I broke the stillness. 'You mentioned a boat. What was that?'

'The boat,' said the Gurnie. 'Ah weel. It's no verra easy this.'

Foxie began, 'Her man was at sea. When they torpedoed him his pey stopped. There was only her and the three wee boys. Twa guid dogs and sheep that kept runnin intae the fucken sea.'

Davie came over, put the pints up and took my note, quietly slipped the change into my hand and waited. Alasdair too, draped elegantly on a bar stool, was listening.

The Gurnie had begun.

'Ye've got to understand, we'd fly out for six hours and back for six hours. All we saw was the sea. Have you any idea how bluidy empty the sea can be? Once, just the once mind, we saw a U-boat but the bugger dived before we could drop even a hand grenade down his hatch.

'And then we'd see the convoys. Ye'd come back and sleep and go out again and they'd still be there. Maybe a hundred miles ahead, maybe no. Usually they'd be smaller than the day before. Ye'd go off to see if you could find a raft or mebbe a boat, though Christ knows how we'd pick them up. That was how we found them.

'They'd set sail and we went down and waggled our wings and they stood and cheered us. They were on a fair course for Kintyre. We came over them again the next day. Still on course. They mebbe didnae see us – we were at fifteen thousand feet – but on they went. It was three days later that they came ashore.

'She was down there for them, twa wee laddies at her skirt, and the bairn at her breast, and the twa dugs yelping – the bitch was Kelpie's mither, ye ken.'

'A guid dug, yon.'

'Aye, guid.' He lifted to drink from his glass and we waited.

'But gentle as the boat had come ashore, they were a' deid, and the gulls had had their een.'

'Cruel the gulls.'

'Aye, cruel. Jist birds though, they canna help it.'

He paused and put the glass back on the table. 'They buried them in the kirkyerd, and she'd aye go up and stand there. It was like she could see how her man had gone.'

'Aye.'

Then suddenly the Gurnie turned on me and anger in his voice.

'Shall I tell you something else?' he demanded. 'I was there when we burned Hamburg and dae ye ken whit? I enjoyed it. I fucken enjoyed frying the bastards. Ach, son, ye can try but ye'll never begin to understand. I hope ye niver dae. If it was worth anything it was that – so that nane of youse wad ever ken enough to understand. It's no much, but it helps me sleep.'

'That's terrible,' said Alasdair into the silence.

'Aye,' said the Gurnie. 'I ken.'

Stuart B. Campbell

THE BURNING

From Bodie of Gight, cooper:
two fir and iron barrels,
for sixteen shillings and eight pence.
>   For him: a balm of lavender, howood
>   and clary sage to ease his twisted back.

From Archie Strachan, coal-merchant:
six bushels of coal,
for twentyfour shillings.
>   For him: a poultice, applied hot, and
>   the pony-man's whisper to calm his gelding.

From Ship-wright Sandy out of Sodom:
four barrels of tar,
for twentysix shillings and eight pence.
>   For him: a draught, which burned
>   like brandy and ginger, to calm his chest.

From Jamie Duguid the chandler:
four fathoms of tow,
for four shillings.
>   For him: turning his unborn baby in
>   its mother's belly; it is not baptised yet.

From Doddie Milne of Mosstown:
twenty loads of peat,
for forty shillings.
>   For him: her voice called through
>   the haar, though she was not seen.

From Willie Bremner, woodcutter:
a stake and the dressing of it,
for sixteen shillings.
>   For him: a luckenbooth of ash and
>   hawthorn which he wore to find a wife.

From Fraser Cruickshank of Strichen:
a bogie and horse for carting the makings,
for eight shillings and four pence.
    For him: after seven years of marriage,
    after his wife went to her, a son.

To Murray Sangster, Justice of the Peace:
for the trial and execution of the warrant,
thirteen shillings and four pence.
    For him: the burning reduces every
    -thing, even guilt, to the ordinary.

Michael Chromy

MY LAST DAY AT SCHOOL

The world hadn't always been like this. Back through Cenozoic, Mesozoic, Palaeozoic to Precambrian. It was different then. Volcanoes ruptured barren landscapes and the world stank of sulphur. Sea worms threaded their way through crinoids and sponges on the ocean floor. Ammonites spiralled around giant murky sea scorpions. Land masses plated up on each other while cockroaches and millipedes began to colonise the planet. Fire and ice. Dinosaurs eventually roaming around right where I was sitting. It must have been brilliant. I wish I'd been alive then.

My mum sat in the chair where she always sat. She was still in her sickly blue water-stained dressing gown. She was ill. She had to rest a lot. She'd probably been sitting there all day watching the telly. She went on watching the telly and didn't even answer when I spoke. Her face just made expressions which said things like 'that's interesting' or 'really?' or 'later'. She was dead quiet these days. She hardly ever said anything. She might as well have just slept twenty-four hours a day. I went into the kitchen to look for something to eat and to draw pictures of dinosaurs. There was an eruption of dirty dishes in the sink. Grease had dripped and congealed on dinner plates. I made a crater with some dirty dreggy cups and fast flowing liquid lava trails ran down quickly to the soupy broth which lay at the bottom of the brown basin. The bin was overflowing and stinking so I gathered it all up and took it out and emptied it into the big bin at the back door. One the kitchen table a T. Rex fought a bloody battle with a Stegosaurus. There was only ever going to be one winner.

I took the pictures into school the next day. Our teacher, Theropod, said she'd put them on the wall. But she never did. She put them on her table and hissed that I could take a sweet. She always had sweets in a clear plastic jar on her table. Sometimes I used to just sit and stare at them. She used them as bait. They were brilliant colours and all mixed up and piled up on top of each other. I could see marshmallow twists and flying saucers and others wrapped up in shiny paper. You got one if you deserved it. You always got what you deserved in this class. I kept my sweet in my pocket till we were outside in the drizzly rain and then I held it out to Amy. Her eyes went wide and we laughed. I wasn't sure why. Maybe we were laughing at different things.

After playtime we got out our reading books. Theropod stalked about the room. When it was Amy's turn to read I wished I could trace the words out into her head for her. She was slow and made mistakes and the teacher didn't give her enough time. I wished she would stop shouting at her. I wished the others in the pack would stop laughing.

There was an incident during lunch. After we were back in class the teacher told Beckie and Amy to stand beside her table. Beckie had got some fresh clothes from the store and was holding her own muddied garb in a plastic bag. When Theropod asked Beckie what happened she just started squealing again. Amy was vulnerable. No hiding place, no camouflage. I tried to think of a way to save her. Theropod went mad. Beckie was like Theropod's own child. It was like a chance she'd been waiting for. Theropod circled Amy, going on and on and on. Ripping her apart. Amy looked so small. She just stared at the floor. I had to do something. I lied. I told Theropod that Beckie had started it. I told her that Beckie had called her a name and then struck the first blow.

'What name?' she growled. As her eyes went to the ceiling then swooped down. 'You're a liar,' her expression said. I stayed calm.

'A bad name, Miss. A really bad name,' I said. I didn't know whether I was going to say it. If I could say it. The Theropod rose up in front of me. She was twenty feet tall, her tail flicking back and forth behind her.

'What name?' she roared. 'What name?' Her head began to slowly rotate around a stationary point right between her eyes. She waited for my reply. My heart was thudding. I could smell her breath.

I said the name. A long, long time ago at another school, in another place, someone else got called a name. Everybody had heard it. Even the master. The culprit was never seen or heard of again. I could think of nothing else. I said that Amy had been called the same name. She looked at me, her head cocked to one side. I thought for a minute she was going to burst out laughing. She sent Amy to the Lizard King and then she hissed that what I'd just said would get somebody into a lot of trouble. I knew by her proximity and the smell of her breath who it was going to be.

My mum asked what I had done at school. I lied. She turned her head to look over at me. Then she smiled and said she was really tired and could I not talk to her just now. She sounded funny. She had got dressed though and there was some new stuff in the fridge. I wished she'd get better. I thought she would have got better when my dad went away. But she didn't. In fact, she got worse.

I went out to play like I always did. I ran over the road and through the hole in the fence and into the park. Near the trees there was a place you could sit between the fence and the hedge and watch everybody. Nobody could see you. Two big ones came in for a drink. I watched them wander around and then head over to a group of younger ones who scattered as they approached. The two big ones sat on a bench and tossed the big brown bottle they'd been drinking from. Then they started pushing each other. Like dinosaurs. The one with the shaved head pushed the other one down and then they started fighting. They thrashed around and rolled down into a gully. The one who'd started it got up first and sank his teeth into the throat of the other one who was still lying on the ground. He never got up again. There was blood everywhere. The shaved head dragged the other one's lifeless body off into the bushes and ate it.

It was dark when I got home. The light was still on in the living room but there was no noise from the telly. I thought at first my mum must have gone to bed but then I heard voices. She was talking to somebody. I waited in the kitchen till the voice was gone. My mum came into the kitchen with an empty glass. I noticed she was in her dressing gown again. I asked her who that had been. She didn't answer.
    She started asking me weird stuff and talking about things I didn't understand. I told her to stop but she wouldn't. I felt scared. She said everything would be all right. I said, 'What are you talking about?' She went to bed. She shouted down, 'Just stick around – okay? Everything'll be fine. Just be here.'
    I wanted to go upstairs but I was too scared. I fell asleep watching the telly and woke up in the middle of the night. It

was dead quiet. As I crept upstairs I thought I heard something. Like a cough. I stopped outside her door to listen. I must have imagined it. There was nothing.

The next day it was pouring. Even though I ran all the way to school I was still late. I didn't even go to the shop. Amy wasn't in. Neither was our teacher. It was the Lizard King. He told me it would be a while before I'd be seeing my pal again. Then another teacher I'd never seen before came in and he went away. The new teacher had scaly skin and claws which were curved like sickles. I could smell her. Like iron. Like blood. Amy's empty chair drew her attention. She came over for a closer look. I felt like she was trying to hypnotise me. Beckie smiled across from her clearing, all safe.

I was starving. I wished now I had just gone to the shop. My mum had still been sleeping when I left. I didn't try to wake her up. I didn't even go into her room. I didn't have time. When I left the house I pulled the door gently shut behind me. A woman who lived across the road waved at me as usual as I ran past.

The Sickle told us our normal teacher would be back tomorrow. She was still digesting Amy. It had stopped raining by playtime. I went round the back of the school on my own and waited. Nobody even noticed. I just stood there. The noise of everybody else in the playground was drifting over the roof and seemed to be coming from the sky. I looked up and watched all the different shades of grey moving at different speeds. I kept on looking. I wondered who would ever trace out the answers for Amy now. I thought about my mum. A bell rang in the sky and I listened to the noise from the playground slowly deaden to silence. I started to shiver. I stayed where I was.

I got back home and unlocked the door. I knew right away. I went up the stairs and stood outside her room. I couldn't hear anything so I slowly pushed the door open. She was lying with her face to the wall. The curtains were still shut. I walked over and said her name but she didn't answer. I sat on the bed but she didn't move. I leant over and pushed her hair off her face. Her skin was cold. I climbed in beside her. I had to heat her up. Fire and ice. It made no difference what happened millions of years ago. It was still the same. The world had always been like this. Always would be. I put my arms around my mum and whispered, 'I'm here.'

Ian Crockatt

JUDAS

I never betrayed my wife
but my haunted friends did
wound her with passionless footage
of my mouth discovering His.

3 days it hung between us,
the suspect O
of my lips, its noose
of puckered flesh as permanently binding

as a Bedouin's kiss.
'So what if you clipped
their improbable lord,' she sniffed,
leaving for the synagogue

and her mother's. Dear tree
I don't know where to put myself;
don't tremble me
out of your arms, I'm not ready.

I see a field of clods,
domes and a peopled hill,
the carpenter weighing nails.
God's Life I never betrayed her,

never will...

Loren Cruden

WINTERKILL

No blame –
it just happens:
I hear coyotes
        exulting over their discovery
and in the morning
the dog starts
bringing home bones
one by one
like the days
until spring.

Criosaidh Dick

DILEAB

Bha i na sìneadh anns a' *bhath*, a com fon uisge agus a ceann ri tacsa ceann a' *bhath*. 'S e *bath* mòr seann fhasanta bh' ann. Fhuair iad e nuair a thàinig a' chiad ghrantaichean a-mach airson taighean nan croitearan a leasachadh. Bha a mathair, uair no dhà, a' beachdachadh air fear ùr fhaiginn ach bha h-athair na aghaidh. 'S e duine mòr, foghainteach a bh' ann agus bha e ag radh nach fhaigheadh e sìneadh a-mach ceart anns na bathaichean ùra bha iad a' deanamh an diugh.

'S ann geal a bha am *bath* agus bha i na sìneadh gu socair agus a làmhan sìos ri taobh. Bha e dìreach mar gum biodh tu ann an ciste-laighe agus i air a lìnigeadh le sìoda geal ach gum biodh i fuar anns a' chistidh mar a bhiodh Ruairidh Bàn, an nàbaidh. Bha an tiodhlacadh aige ann an diugh. Bha an t-àm aice tighinn a mach às a' bhath. Biodh iad ag èigheach rithe greasad oirre an ceart-uair, a h-athair agus a mathair agus an t-ogha aca, an nighean aice fhein. Bha iad uile a' dol chun an tiodhlacaidh. 'S e deagh nàbaidh a bh' ann an Ruairidh. Bha e mun aon aois ri pàrantan. 'S e bantrach a bh' ann. Chaochail a bhean bho chionn dà bhliadhna. Cha robh clann idir aca.

Bha i leisg tighinn a-mach às a' *bhath*. Bha i cofhurtal na sìneadh anns an uisge bhlàth, chùmhraidh. Bha i cofhurtal na beatha. Bha i air a bhith a' tidseadh anns a' sgoil bheag anns a bhaile seo, i fhein agus aon tidsear eile bho chionn corr is fichead bliadhna. Chan iarradh i an corr. Rinn i suas a h-inntinn nuair a bha i còig bliadhn' deug gu robh i airson a bhith na tidsear agus gu robh i airson a bhith na tidsear anns an sgoil far an robh i fhein nuair a bha i òg. Bha i air a bhith an-sin bhon chrìochnaich i anns a' Cholaisde ach na sia miosan a ghabh i dheth nuair a rugadh Donna Mairi agus 's ann glè ainneamh a dh' fhàg i an t-eilean a' bharrachd. Seo far an robh i ag iarraidh a bhith.

An deidh dhi bhith bliadhna a' tidseadh, bha i air a dhol air saor-laithean dhan Spàinn comhla ri na caraidean a bh' aice anns a' Cholaisde. Bha iad air seo a chur air dòigh anns a' bhliadhna mu dheireadh a bha iad comhla. Bha iad gu bhith cho math dheth, mas fhìor.

Thill i dhachaidh, donn leis a' ghrèin agus air a h-ùrachadh leis na làithean saora agus air a h-inntinn a dhèanamh suas nach

fàgadh i an t-eilean tuilleadh. 'S e samhradh breagha blàth a bh'
ann, anns a h-uile àite, a' bhliadhn' ud.

Air fear dhe na làithean breagha grianach sin, is i a'
faireachdainn caran leisg, chuir i oirre tè dhe na deasachan-
snàmh a bh' aice anns an Spàinn agus leine mhòr le h-athair
air a h-uachdar. Thug i leatha searadair mòr agus an leabhar a
bha i a' leughadh agus chaidh i sìos gu ceann shìos na croite
gu oir a' chladaich. Bha bàgh beag blàth an-sin agus creagan
ga fhasgadh bhon h-uile taobh. Chuir i an searadair sìos air a'
ghainmheach. Bha an làn a-muigh agus bha an tràigh gheal
falamh, eu-coltach ri tràighean na Spàinne, ach gu faiceadh i
Ruairidh Bàn, an nàbaidh, pios uaipe, ag obair air an eathar.
Biodh e a' dol a-mach leatha nuair a dh' eirigh an làn. Bha
boiler-suit air agus leine foipe. Sin a bhiodh air an còmhnaidh.
Bha faoileag no dhà a' sgiathadh os a cionn ach bha iad fhein
caran leisg an diugh. Shuidh i greis a' coimhead a-mach air an
traigh agus a-null chun nam beanntan fad' air falbh. 'S e deagh
chomharra bha sin. Ma bha na beanntan fad' air falbh, bha an
deagh shìde a' dol a mhaireachdainn. Thug i dhith a leine
airson a' ghrian a' leigeil gu com agus rinn i i fhein cofhurtal
air an t-searadair agus thoisich i ri leughadh an leabhair.

An ceann greis, thàinig failleas eadar i agus a' ghrian agus
nuair a thog i a ceann, bha Ruairidh Bàn na sheasamh ri taobh.
"Uill, uill, nach ann aig cuid a tha an saoghal dheth. Ciamar a
chòrd do chuairt riut?"
Shuidh e air a' ghainmheach faisg oirre agus dh' innis i dha gun
do chòrd a turas rithe uamhasach math ach gu robh i toilichte
a bhith dhachaidh.

"'S e fiòr *home bird* a th'annad", thuirt e.

Bha iad a' bruidhinn a-null 's a-nall greis agus iad a' coimhead air a cheile.

"B' fheairrd thu do thuras. Tha a' ghrian air laighe gu mòr
ort. Tha e tighinn math dhuit."

Bha e air tighinn na b' fhaisg' oirre.

Bha i na leth shìneadh air a h- uileann a' coimhead suas na
aodann. Shìn i i fhein a-mach mar chat ga bhlianadh fhein as
a' ghrèin. Bha e cho nàdurra mar a thog i suas a làmhan agus
chuir i mu amhaich iad agus tharraing i e a-nuas gus a pògadh.
Dh' fhàs na pògan na bu mhiannaiche. Thog e a làmh agus
thug e na strapaichean bhar a gualainn agus thoisich e ri
pògadh a ciòchan.

Thog e a cheann agus choimhead e oirre.

"A bheil thu cinnteach gur e seo a tha thu ag iarraidh?"

"Tha, tha mi glè chinnteach."

Chaidh mìos seachad agus da mhiòs agus bha i cinnteach gu robh i trom. Dh' fheumadh i dhol chun an dotair ach cha robh feum aic' air dearbhadh. Bha i air a bhith cinnteach bhon chiad latha gum biodh i trom.

Nuair a dh' innis i dha h-athair is dha mathair bha an cridheachan briste. Cha robh iad airson a creidsinn. Chan innseadh i dhaibh cò leis a bha e. Am b' aithne dhaibh e? An robh seo air tachairt nuair a bha i air falbh air na saor-laithean? An e Spàinnteach a bh' ann? Bha iad a' fàs fiathaich. An e nach robh fhios aice? Mo nàire! Bhiodh gu leòr aig muinntir a' bhaile ri radha.

Thuirt i riutha, nan robh iad airson, gun gluaiseadh i a-mach às an taigh. Gheibheadh i taigh-comhairle. Agus phàigheadh i cuid-eigin airson coimhead as dèidh an leanaibh fhads a bha i ag obair.

Tha fios nach robh dùil aice tilleadh a dh' obair. A h-aghaidh a chur air clann-sgoile. An leigeadh iad leatha tilleadh dhan sgoil?

Ach mu dheireadh striochd iad agus cha robh chrith aice a bhith a' smaoineachadh air a dachaidh fhàgail. Cò b' fheàrr a choimheadadh as a dèidh na a h-athair agus a mathair fhein? Agus nuair a thigeadh an leanabh, nach eil fhios gur ann aig a sheanair agus a sheanmhair a bha còir coimhead as a dheidh cuideachd. Cha robh iad gus a bhith air an nàrachadh buileach glan.

Ma bha muinntir a' bhaile ri foghail, cha tuirt duine guth riuth-san. Biodh i a' cluinntin a mathair a' rànaich uaireanan air feadh na h-oidhche agus a h-athair ga cofhurtachadh, ach beag air bheag, bh' fhàs cùisean na b' fheàrr agus nuair a rugadh an leanabh bha iad cho toilichte agus cho measail oirre agus ged nach biodh na miòsan a chaidh seachad air tachairt riamh.

Dè an t-ainm a bha i a' dol a thoirt oirre? "Bha mi a' smaoineachadh, nam biodh sibh fhein deònach, gun toirinn na h-ainmean agaibh fhein oirre. Donna Mairi – Domhnall agus Mairi." Choimhead a h-athair agus a mathair air a chèile. Bha deòir na suilean. "Chòrdadh sin rinn math dha rireabh," thuirt a h-athair.

Aon latha is a h-athair agus a mathair air falbh fon taigh agus i fhein trang ag obair air leabhraichean sgoile, thog i a h-aire far an tè bhig. Aon mhionaid bha i a' cluich mun doras agus an ath mhionaid cha robh sgial oirre. Chlisg i. Chaill a casan an lùths.

Ach dìreach leis a-sin, nochd an nàbaidh, Ruairidh Bàn, timcheall ceann na bathchadh agus an tè bheag aige air a ghualainn.

"Thachair i rium," ars esan, "a' dèanamh air a chladach."

"O, taing dhan Aigh."

Chuir e sìos Donna Mairi agus chaidh i na ruith a-staigh dhan taigh.

"An ann leamsa tha i? Mas ann, bhithinn deònach gabhail rithe."

'S e duine onarach a bh' ann, smaoinich i.

"Chan ann, 's ann leamsa tha i." Bha i a' smaoineachadh gun tàinig faochadh air aghaidh.

Bha Donna Mairi a-nis fichead bliadhna. Bha an ceathrar ac' air a bhith glè chofhurtal comhla. 'S e mamaidh a bh' aig Donna Mairi oirre-se agus seanair agus seanmhair air a pàrantan. Bha iad an toiseach a' smaointeachadh gum bu chòir do Donna Mairi a bhith a' gabhail mamaidh agus dadaidh orra-san ach thuirt ise gur ann leath-se bha i agus gur e mamaidh a bhiodh aic' oirre.

Ged a dh' fhoighneachd Donna Mairi aig amanan nuair a bha i ag èirigh suas cò b' athair dhi, thuig i mu dheireadh nach robhar a' dol a dh' innse dhi agus stad i. Mas do dh' fhalbh i dhan Oilthigh dh' fhoighneachd i aon uair eile agus cha do dh' fhoighneachd tuilleadh.

Thàinig crith oirre. Bha an t-uisg' air fàs fuar. Seo mar a bhiodh e ann an ciste-laighe. Thàinig i a-mach às a' *bhath* agus thiormaich i i fhein. Chuir i oirre *dressing-gown* agus chaidh i tron chidsin airson a dhol suas an staidhre a chur iompa. Bha h-athair agus a mathair deiseil mar tha. Bha iad na suidhe aig a' bhord ag òl cupa tì. An robh i ag iarraidh cupa? Bha i an àm greasad oirre. Cha robh. Rachadh i a chur iompa.

Bha Donna Mairi a-muigh anns a' ghàrradh. Bha ise deiseil cuideachd. Bha gàrradh breagha aca. Bha a h-athair deidheil air flùraichean. Choimhead i a-mach air an uinneig. Bha Donna Mairi na seasamh agus ròs dearg aice na laimh.

Bha sluagh mòr anns an eaglais. Bha daoine measail air Ruairidh Bàn. Agus bha seasamh aige anns an àite. Ach cha robh càirdean dlùth idir aige. Bha na càirdean a bh' aige caran fad' às. Cha robh duin' ann, a chanadh tu, bhiodh ga chaoidh.

Air an rathad dhachaidh anns a' chàr bha Donna Mairi ag

radh gur e tiodhlacadh uamhasach duilich a bh' ann. "Uill," ars' a seanmhair, "tha a h-uile tiodhlacadh duilich. Tha daoine a' caoidh."

"Sin, ged tha, a tha deanamh an tiodhlacadh seo cho duilich," thuirt Donna Mairi. "Bha Ruairidh Bàn cho laghach agus chan eil duine ga chaoidh." Bha iad uile samhach airson greis. "Thug e litir dhomhsa mas do dh' fhalbh mi dhan Oilthigh. Dh' iarr e orm a cur air falach agus gun innse do dhuine. Agus thug e orm gealltainn nach leughainn i gus am biodh e marbh agus air a thiodhlacadh."

"Tha sin annasach," thiurt a seanmhair. "Saoil dè th'as an litir?" An do dh fhosgail thu i?

"Cha do dh' fhosgail. Gheall mi dha nach fosglainn i gus am biodh an tiodhlacadh aige seachad. Thug e orm mionnachadh."

Cha tuirt i facal agus cha chanadh.

Nuair a chaidh iad dhachaidh, chaidh Donna Mairi suas an staidhre a dh' iarraidh na litreach.

Bha e air a' chroit agus na beathaichean agus an taigh – taigh breagha cloiche – agus an eathar agus na bha aige anns a' bhanca fhagail aice. Cha robh an corr anns an litir. Cha tuirt duine facal.

"'S e m' athair a bh' ann, nach e? Bha còir aig cuid-eigin a bhith air innse dhomh."

John Duffy

SWEET HEART OF JESUS

Ma grandpa sung *The Green Isle of Erin* at a Masonic dinner in the toon and got an encore. That must have been in nineteen oatcake, for Ah can never remember seeing the man, he died when Ah was a wean. Ma voice is the same as his but, the daddy used to tell me that, an Ah do enjoy singing, but the setting's got to be right.

Sometimes ye might be at a party, an ye can sing an sing, but next week, the same folk, same place, an ye jist canny get it started.

Ah don't like singing in the nick, maybe when ye're on yer tod, a wee quiet old favourite, or something that's been birlin roun in yer heid for days an days; or jist now an again, if somebody's got a wee concert goin, you know, guys thegither, jist remembrin auld songs. But mainly it's keep the heid doon, eyes doon, coont doon tae release. Ye're on yer own.

Once ye're through that gate, ye're on yer own as well. Ah always imagined – still do – the jile shakin as the door slams shut behind me, and the word goin roon – *McCandless is oot!* Con an screw thegither, passin the word roon.

Truth is, from inside ye canny see the drive or hear the gate, and anybody that is anybloodybody in there doesny know who Ah am an widny care.

Like a hunner thousan guys afore me, Ah turn roon at the end of the drive an curse Barlinnie an feel that stupit daen it. Ye mutter some dire oath at the big black walls, an the echo comes skitin back ower the field at ye, for baith you an the jile know fine ye'll be back.

But dire oaths have their uses, for ye want to pit a distance between yersel and thon big hulk on the hill. Ye feel really obvious at first, an ye canny stoap gawpin, no jist at the wimmen, but the trams, the weans, the dugs.

Time was when Ah hid sumbdy tae meet me when Ah come oot, the brother or the wife, an wance, Goad help us, ma mammy turned up wi money an a coat. She'd have had blankets an hot soup an all if she could have got the stove up on the tram. Ach well, nae mair o that, an if truth be told, Ah need that time walkin doon tae toon tae adjust tae the ootside again.

Always walk it. Ye're savin the fare, ye're on yer own, ye

don't huv tae be pointed oot on the tram as sumbdy that jist got oot the jile, an while folk might start sympathetic, the magic wears off eftir a couple a stops.

Ye go past some toff hooses an the school an the chapel, then some corporation hooses, then Ah always nip through the park. It's quicker, ye can stay oot a folk's way, an Ah've got a wee scheme that lets me arrive back in Toonheid in style.

When ye staun at the flagpole in Ally Park, ye have they big gasometers at Blochairn on yer right, the road tae Edinburgh an the Cathkin Braes tae yer left, an in front, aw the chimney pots between there an the toon.

When Ah come doon intae Dennistoun Ah like tae check the streets – no too busy, no too bright suits me best, for then the backcoorts are quiet, weans at school or indoors, men away tae work, wummen maybe gettin the dinners ready.

There are some toff red tenements that are useless, they've got phones, they'll get on tae the polis, *There's some man up to no good in our beck green*, an the next thing is yer auld freens are movin ye on. Naw, always go to the working class.

Ye want invisibility, no tae be startin with some wumman cleanin her windaes or hinging oot her washin right by ye, so Ah like tae squint along the backs tae find a likely lookin empty spot, an then Ah start.

Burns is always good. *Banks an braes*, or *Annie Laurie*. It gets folk on your side, they can aw mind their daddy or Uncle Josie givin it laldy at Hogmanay, an it's slow, an gies ye the chance tae get the feel of how it sounds. Wi some tenements ye can sing an never hear it, but Ah know the best places.

Always move on eftir wan, or at the maist, two. Ye might miss the odd bob or two, but it's wan o the obvious rules that ye've no tae make a pest o yersel. An folk doon the street want ye tae come an do somethin for them.

Ye're lookin up at the windaes, seein whit curtains are movin, but no seemin tae pay attention. You are not beggin. You are an act. A windae'll open jist a wee bit, six inches or so, an a thrupenny bit comes doon. Ye keep singin, but acknowledge it wi a wee salute. Then some wifie thinks, *Ah'm no lettin her be the only generous wan up this close*, an tuppence, wrapped up in a poke or a bit torn oot the paper, follows the first yin. At the end of the song, say *thank you* quietly, pick up the cash, and nip into the next back coort, or the wan eftir that. Another popular wan, *Bonnie Scotland I adore thee, though*

I'm far across the sea, an here it comes.

Near the end o that street, Ah'll dae T*he Lord's my shepherd* or *The old rugged cross*, an get some protestant money. In a couple of minutes Ah'm in the next street, they've been listenin tae, an Ah dae something teuchtery like *Westerin home*, then since the catholics have been listenin an waitin, Ah gie them some o the hymns that were hammered intae us as weans –

> *Sweet heart of Jesus,*
> *fount of love and mercy,*
> *today we come, thy blessing to implore;*
> *oh touch our hearts, so cold and so ungrateful...*

an aw the wee bits of change they've stashed on the windysill come doon, so Ah finish off, head up the canal, that'll bring me oot tae aw the pubs an bookies in Parson Street, where sumbdy'll tell me what's goin on. An Ah might even run intae the wife.

Who knows, we might negotiate a truce, get wan o they new hooses in a scheme, an land a job as the Lord Provost's Tea Boy. Jist for the moment, though, Ah'm walkin the canal bank, fingerin the change in ma pocket, tryin tae add it up tae a higher figure than whit's actually there, and singing *Hail, queen of heaven*, though there's naebody aboot tae hear me:

> *remi-ind thy Son*
> *that He-e has paid*
> *THE price*
> *of ou-r*
> *in-i-qui-ty.*

Magi Gibson

SAND

the wet sand
the sea has lain on
bears imprints of weed and kelp

like your skin in the morning
marked by the tangles
of my hair

SNOWFLAKE

snowflake on my tongue
cold white kiss
tumbled from heaven

how easily you melt
my indifference

ROBIN

on a white pillow
of puffed up snow
the robin's breast
pulses
red, fast
as my heart
when
I think
of you

Rody Gorman

LUATH

Rinn sinn ur gleidheadh
Mu dheireadh thall nur luaith
Am broinn crogain
Ann an gàrradh
Air cùl cloiche
Còmhla ri ur cuideachd is an fheadhainn eile

Bhon – thoiribh mathanas dhuinn! –
Gur h-e rinn sinn dheth
Nan d' rachadh ur cur fo chab lice
Dìreach mar chàch
Gun èaladh ur n-aigne mhòr às
Agus gun d' rachadh ur sgapadh
Thar ar comais
Bhuainn air feadh na cruinne.

ashes

wepreservedyouintheendinajarinthegardendyke
behindastonealongwithyourfolksandtherestbe
causewereckonedthatifyouwereputunderaslab
liketherestyourgreatspiritwouldbreakoutandy
ouwouldbescatteredallo025theuniverse

DEALBH

A' sealltainn
Ri dealbh
Dubh is geal
Is glas
An là sin a phòs iad,

A bhios gu sìorraidh
A' tuiteam fo sgaoil
Far nan uileann san leabhar air a dhòthadh
Ris a bheil e 'n ceangal –
Chì mi cuideigin ag obair orra,
Gam bogadh ann an uisge san t-seòmar-dhorcha –

Chìthear an sàl 's na bìdeagan confetti a rinn iad a thilgeil
As an dèidh
Mar nòs

Agus an siaban sèidte
Sgapte mun rèidhlean ud
Mar mhire
Stòlda bean-is-fear-na-bainnse
A' falbh le gaoith far a chèile
'S ag aomadh ri chèile mar aon.

poorspectrefaceshapeimagestatue

lookingatthepictureblackandwhiteandgreyoftheirwedding
daywhichisforeverfallingloosefromthecornersinthesinged
bookwheretheyrekepticanseesomebodyworkingonthemsoft
steepingtheminrainywaterinthedarkroomoneseesthebrine
andbitsofconfettiwhichtheythrewasisthecustomandthespin
driftaboutthelawnliketherestrainedecstacyofbrideandgroom
driftingapartandcomminglingatthesametime

Charlie Gracie

WAITING

I hope you are happy, John Mills
as I scuff
across your hall
into your room.

Beside the fire your pants hang on a horse
slippers, worn unevenly, stand on the edge of the hearth
half on
half off.

On a table, evidence of nurses
and the smell of everything
wiped and scrubbed and sanitised.

A dresser stands, all shiny dark wood and curved edges
brassy handles hanging
silent
solemn
still.

The fire coughs soot from its dry black throat.

Your chair stares expectantly at the door.

DEAD ON THE HILL

If I were you I'd be sad to be found.
Announced, un-named, on the news.
Carted in a bag to the road.
Patched in places crows have been
to be seen by a weeping wife.

No.
I want the crows to feast.
I want to seep into the earth
the worms to work my flesh.
I want to feed the roots of blaeberries
to trickle gently down green braes.
I want my picked bones to splinter
and my dust to be lifted
by the breath of the cold wind.

I want to stare
still as the watchful hill
at the foreverness of the stars beyond.

Yvonne Gray

CASTLE O BURRIAN

Puffins, windblown, come careering
in, wings a-tilt,
bright feet braced,
outstretched to catch
the ledge. They gather in rows
on narrow balconies,
tiny, gaudy, gossiping gods,
paintbox beaks a-gabble,
heads tweaking to this side
and that as they spotlight
what comings? what goings?
among guillemot groundlings
below. For now it's all
comedy, circus, spectacle,
the waves' drumthunder
an off-stage roll, the stormclouds
curtained back. The great black-backed's
cloak is folded:
its murderous eyes
look elsewhere.

THE NEW RAM

All hell is out tonight.
The wind blatters about the walls
and rain shards spike the stones.

Across the rafters ice-eyed rats
scatter, nail-like claws scaling
the cross-beam.

And with the turmoil broiling above,
we in the stall's sharn and gutter
regard the young ram.

Back and fore he treads, restless,
nostrils flaring, eye whites gleaming.
Then, caught, he stands

at last, contained by your hand
cupped firmly under his jaw.
His springy wool is creamy richness;

his legs clipped, broad-boned, hard;
his hooves trim, lacquered black,
placed four-square.

At a standstill, for now, we three watch
amid the straw's trampled gold,
bathed in the glow

of the light
that swings beneath
the storm-tossed roof-tree.

Francis Green

BEAUTIFUL

Alice is one of those ideas-above-her-station tarty kinds. An office girl who thinks she is all sweetness and roses. Beautiful, in a conventional way. Blonde. Pretty. Good body. Sexy walk, and when she's close enough a subtle, flowery smell. We used to get on, share a joke, so one time I asked her if she wanted to go for a drink after work, without meaning anything, just a drink and she said 'no'. Didn't give a reason. Just 'no thanks', brushing it off just like she gets asked every day and Madam is tired of being asked, and then I get called inside to fix a pipe on the warehouse floor and Madam saunters off, and I don't get the chance to explain I meant just a drink.

Then I see her the next day and she acts like nothing happened. Above it all, like it doesn't matter. She comes over all airy, in her fancy clothes and she makes a joke about 'no rest for the wicked' whilst I'm sweeping the yard, so I deliberately am off with her, stubborn and quiet whilst she acts like we are still friends, but we can't be friends. Don't friends sometimes go for a drink after work?

And it carries on like that for a few days, maybe a week. Her being 'everything's normal' and flirting about, and me keeping dignified, polite even but not friendly. Then one night, my car packs up on the way home. Cuts out. And I'm beside it trying to flag someone down and she drives by, sees me and reverses back up. She gets out of her car looking all dainty and says 'Can I help?' all patronising, like she knows anything about cars. So she's rummaging about in her boot for jump leads and then I'm behind her and I tear off her shirt and put my hand over her mouth, even though there is no one around to hear. Underneath my hand I can feel her trying to open her mouth and scream and her eyes are watering and all begging, and I put my hand up her skirt and pull off her knickers. They are thin, cotton and blue. And I push her back against the car.

A few days after that I get called to the office to mop up a load of coffee. Madam burst out crying and dropped a tray full and gets sent home. And I have to clear up after her. She hasn't been back in a couple of days. I'm not worried. She's too vain to tell anyone. She's probably taken a little holiday or sick leave. She's probably sitting at home watching *Neighbours* on full pay whilst I'm stuck here having to fix a broken lock in the women's toilets. I hate going in the women's toilets. Like a pervert. The door's jammed, and the office girls have started to grumble about the smell, but it's not jammed, it's locked from the inside. So I unscrew the lock on the outside and push it through. The door swings open and the smell hits me and I look up and there she is, hanging from the ceiling, her face all bloated and blue, like punch bruises, like she's been pumped full of water. The smell of shit and dead animals hits me again in the face. She stares out, her eyes white and bulging empty, and the rope has welted thick, red and purple, into her neck. I'm trying to think, and I close the door. She is not beautiful any more.

Roddy Hamilton

MARCH OF THE GIANTS

Audrey looked at her watch and spent a few minutes tapping things. The newly arrived newspapers on the counter, the plastic see-through case of the bakery basket. Just tapping them.

From where she was she looked across and out through the window blinds. The street was empty, the sun strong enough on the tarmac to make it look like snow if you imagined. But there was no traffic.

Across the road was the exhaust and tyre-fitting place. Audrey had been running the shop long enough to remember when it had been tenements with real people living inside. Behind the shop had also once been tenements. That seemed like a long time ago. Now they had become a residential home for the elderly.

When the traffic finally came it came slowly, like a procession. It was fronted by a column of tractors and other farm vehicles. There were lorries and pick-up trucks and delivery vans. They were moving at a snail's pace. Some of the boys in the cabs were sounding their horns or klaxons. It was like a very dismal carnival.

The hubbub roused Henry. He'd been sitting in the back shop reading the paper. Whenever Henry read the paper the pages shook with his fingers. He struggled through the partition of coloured plastic strips. He stood grinding his teeth from side to side, looking out the window. The coloured strips behind him tapped against each other and came together like hippy lovers.

'What's all that?' Henry said.

Business that morning was slow. From half eight until a quarter to ten the traffic went nose to tail. It was travelling so slowly you could pass it by breaking into a jog. No-one stopped their cars outside the shop. Perhaps they were worried they might not get back in the stream of traffic. Audrey's only customers were Mrs Riach (who bought a newspaper) and a couple of young lads from the tyre place (who came in for their usual rolls and milk). There was no sign of Inspector Young yet.

About ten, Audrey went upstairs to go and find Melanie. Melanie was still in her nightdress. Audrey found her holding Gruber above the bathroom sink.

I can't believe he loves water, Mum, Melanie said.

Audrey thought it was about time Melanie was dressed. She told her so. She told her Henry would give her a lift to the cash and carry. Melanie stopped what she was doing. Gruber ran away. Melanie grinned and wiped her hands down the front of her nightdress then began brushing her teeth.

When they'd gone in the car, Audrey had a cup of strong tea. She warmed her hands around the cup. The traffic had returned to normal. On the radio they were saying it was the fault of the road hauliers. The hauliers were protesting about the high level of duty on fuel. They had driven slowly along all routes into the city in protest. They said they were hoping to cause Maximum Disruption. As part of the protest they'd stopped all the lorries carrying petrol from the oil refineries. Outside Audrey's shop the wind began to unsettle the leaves on the chestnut trees. Autumn was coming.

Audrey liked summer. There was a sense of community which didn't exist any other time. In summer people left their windows open. You could hear their conversations float across the streets and under the cherry trees. In summer Audrey felt closer to the world.

The cars passed by now with one unending groan.

Special edition! the man shouted, Fuel crisis!

He climbed back in his van and was driving away before Audrey could say anything. Under the awning, on the pavement, were the evening papers tied in string. They usually came out in the afternoon but the newspaper makers had brought this forward to the morning because the fuel crisis was such an interesting story. Everyone wanted to know about it, the man on the telephone had said. It affected everybody. He added she could order more papers if she phoned the circulation office.

None of the morning newspapers was bought. Audrey sold her first evening paper at a little past eleven. To Mr Grant. Mr Grant was a retired decorator but he could still do a job for you if you paid in cash. Mr Grant had painted the whole front shop for Audrey. And apart from a few brush hairs set in the gloss and the odd patch where the old colour showed, he'd done quite a good job.

Puts you in mind of the days of the marches, doesn't it, Audrey?

Mr Grant waved his newly bought paper as if it was a flag.

My brother in law – he just phoned to say when he got into work. An hour and thirty minutes it took him the eight miles!

Mr Grant made a *tcha!* sound.

There was still no sign of Inspector Young by twelve o'clock. This wasn't unusual. She'd hoped he'd visit while Henry and Melanie were out but that didn't happen. She began to worry about Henry and Melanie. Then she told herself it was probably the traffic snarl-up somewhere on the way.

Just as she was thinking this, the car pulled up outside, laden down in the back with boxes from the cash and carry. Audrey had worked out there was enough petrol left in the tank for another ten or so of these trips if things didn't improve. That would be sufficient. It didn't include other trips, but where else would they need to go? She had enough of the heavier stuff to last a lifetime. The cans of soup and beans and everything stored downstairs were only slightly out of date and would last a while. They wouldn't need to be discounted for another month.

All the new stuff from the back of the car they put downstairs, box by box. Henry was no good at lifting. That was understandable. His walking since the accident was a series of stumbles strung together. It was painful for Audrey to watch. She could see the determination on his face as he crossed the room.

Oh, Henry, not there!

Henry left a box of bin liners on the floor in front of the counter. Melanie moved the liners through to the back shop. Audrey didn't let Henry sit down. He could stay with the till, she said, while she looked over the receipts and stapled them into the book. She told him it hadn't been busy the whole day. There was nothing to worry about. She didn't want to hear anything about cash compartments in the till drawer being too small for his fingers, or five pences being too fiddly for him. If he needed anything she was only a step away behind the screen made of the coloured plastic strips in the back shop.

Audrey sat down on a little chair beside the Super Ser heater which wasn't on. She began to write numbers down in her book. She shunned the small calculator which was on the desk in front of her. She did it all in her head instead, looking up the columns of boxes which contained toilet rolls and cereal boxes and half shutting her eyes. Halfway through one of the calculations came a loud noise from the front shop.

Behind the till there were sandwiches everywhere on the floor. She bent down to pick them back up. Egg and corned beef and cheese and ham sandwiches all still in their cling film.

She was looking at Henry's beige flannels and brown shoes. He made an effort to bend down but she put a hand up to stop him. 'It's okay,' she said. Once all the sandwiches were back in their box she put the tray back on the counter.

Here, she said, and she held out to her husband one of the sandwiches whose wrapper seemed to be looser than the rest, Have this one for your lunch.

Although it was still wrapped in its cling film, Henry didn't like the look of the sandwich. He stared at Audrey. His teeth were grinding from side to side. Audrey thought he might be trying to say something. But if he had something to say surely he would just say it. There was nothing to it. You just opened your mouth and talked.

I'll make us a cup of tea, she said.

There were only a few customers at lunch time. Most of the sandwiches sold, but after a while it went completely quiet again. She didn't have to phone the circulations office for more copies of the evening paper.

After she had finished with the books and had had herself a sandwich she sent Henry upstairs where he could sleep. Melanie was running herself a bath.

Look, Mum. Look at Gruber.

Melanie! said Audrey, You're thirty-nine years old.

Melanie suspended Gruber above the water with his paws just touching it. He hardly moved until Audrey came nearer and turned off the taps. Then he struggled to free himself. Audrey could hear the television from the room next door. A lot of clapping and shouting was coming from it.

Let him down, said Audrey.

But he loves it, said Melanie, I just can't believe how much he loves the water!

Gruber was now sitting on the windowsill licking his paws. On the windowsill beside him was a bubble bath bottle. Its lid was the shape of Top Cat. Gruber didn't notice. Melanie dropped her clothes. Naked, she clapped Gruber and poured some liquid from the Top Cat bottle into the bath, then she stepped in. Her skin folded at the stomach and her breasts hung down over the water. Gruber looked at Melanie as she began to clean herself. Audrey couldn't think of anything else to say. It was about two fifteen.

Eventually Inspector Young did come in. Audrey had been restocking the confectionery rack. Chocolate bars at the back, children's sweets at the front. She had already put out the last of the cat food and firelighters. Someone phoned about a second-hand freezer cabinet. Would she like one? they asked. She told them she already had a new one, which was true, except that the new one had also been second-hand.

She was surprised to see Inspector Young so late in the day. Usually he came in the late morning. She saw his jacket was buttoned and what she could see of his white shirt was well ironed. His trousers were pressed and his shoes clean. She smiled at him as he came in. He didn't talk straight away. He waited until the door chime had stopped completely. Inspector Young always seemed to take his time like that. Audrey thought it gave him a towering authority. Inspector Young walked over to the counter and put the fingers of his right hand on it.

How are you? he said.

She tilted her head to one side ever so slightly and then felt for the beads which were always around her throat. Then she replied, Fine.

It's an awful thing, isn't it? he said, and Inspector Young gestured with a nod of his head at the newspapers, a few of which were left on the counter. They're running out all over the place. Some places they're restricting sales to six litres. It puts you in mind of the seventies.

Inspector Young stood a good foot above Audrey's standing height. Behind him, she caught the topmost edge of the window and the awning outside which rippled in the breeze. Then Audrey spotted a single white hair on his shoulder. She wanted to reach up and pluck the hair and brush down the shoulder of his jacket.

Quite a few officers have run out of petrol, he said.

I expect your boys will have special rations for petrol, Audrey said.

Yes. For patrol cars, obviously. We can't have *them* without petrol.

I heard the supermarkets are running out of bread, she said. Got time for a cup of tea? She wondered if he would have time. His moustache was trimmed very short. She couldn't decide if he needed his haircut yet. He definitely had new cufflinks.

Not today, I'm afraid. My partner's in the car. He's waiting outside. I'll have my usual cigarettes, Audrey.

Twenty?

That's right.

She took his brand from the shelf and held it in the air above the counter. Simultaneously, Audrey prodded the amount into the till. Inspector Young opened his top jacket button and reached inside for his wallet. He took out a bank-note and passed it to Audrey. She released the cigarettes into his hand without looking up. Then, just as she was about to put the money in the till, he said, How's Henry? And Melanie?

Audrey opened the till drawer. It made a tiny money noise. Oh, *you* know, she said.

She rolled her eyes upwards. She fished out his change. Her small fingers fit in the compartments with no problems and she took his change and held it very close to her chest.

Henry's still having some difficulty lifting the heavier things, she said.

You ought to be careful, said Inspector Young. Doing it all yourself. He wagged a finger.

Audrey held on to his change like it was a talisman.

Yes. Well, she said, and drew a sigh which sounded like dust settling.

Don't forget. If you want me to look at your security, the offer stands. I could look at your windows. Can't be too careful, these days.

She glanced at the trapdoor which led down to the basement. She suddenly thought about all the out of code stock in boxes there.

Inspector Young glimpsed the money which was tightly enmeshed in her hand. Eventually she handed it over. Her arms were thin and her hands showed the tendons through the skin. Her breathing was shallow. She pressed the money into his hands and briefly felt the roughness of his palm.

Melanie thinks she can teach the cat to swim.

Inspector Young chuckled and put the cigarettes in his pocket. He put the note into his wallet and the change into his trouser pocket and said goodbye. Audrey watched the car pull away.

About five o'clock, the hauliers came back. Henry was up from his sleep and Melanie had gone out for a walk. The road was quiet for a few minutes in the out-of-town direction and then they came back. At the front were the tractors. They were followed by the van drivers and the truckers and trailer drivers. They pumped their horns in defiance.

Since Henry was awake, Audrey asked him to look after the

till while she went outside for a moment. She went out the door and stood beneath the awning, looking up at the procession. Some of the cab drivers waved at her. She followed them up the road a short distance. The queue of traffic snaked back about a quarter of a mile and then disappeared behind the tenements. Some of them had banners on them to do with the dispute. In between some of the lorries were ordinary cars but they couldn't get past to overtake the lorries. Audrey watched this for long enough that the breeze caused her to fold her arms close to her chest. She walked until she came to the place where the other grocer's shop had been. There she stopped with her arms still tightly folded, thumbs hooked inside her cardigan, looking along the line of traffic.

George Inglis

SOME NEWS

I'm trying to think of some news for you like you asked. I'm sitting out the back of the kitchen smoking, and you're over there, and I'm managing well, you'll be pleased to know (relieved to know?), and my hands are fucked with washing so many dishes what with the tourists and all that although there aren't as many as last year for some reason but the weather's pretty crap so far this year so that'll not be helping, and big Bernie's in there banging about with the pots and pans and baking trays as usual and cursing like a lunatic and telling the new guy he's a useless wanker; Teri's on her period and threatening to join Bernie's mouth to his arsehole with a flick of the boning knife if he doesn't shut his filthy mouth (the pot and the kettle, eh?); Sandra's just found out she's got two resits and is eyeing up the bottle of paracetamol on the window sill; Iain's prancing around taking orders in his sister's tartan skirt making out it's a kilt, but the tourists know fuck all anyway, he says (as we know all too well); and the till's twenty quid short already and if it's not found by the end of the day Kenny says we're all sacked, again, and he's got a new set of false teeth that makes him look like he's breaking them in for a horse, all white and nearly jumping out his mouth when he speaks and it's hard not to laugh but we know he'll go mental if we do.

I'm drawing deep on my fag, sipping my scalding hot coffee from the mug, staring at that damp patch on the outhouse wall that I still think looks like Harpo Marx in profile. And then, because I'm missing you, I'm staring at your name tattooed in Indian ink on the back of my left hand – JEAN – as if you need reminded of your own name – and it was fucking sore even though I was pissed – which accounts for the misshapen N – because I was near comatose by then – and when I told you and showed you you went berserk, like I'd never seen you before, like a mad woman, a woman in a frenzy, and then you didn't speak to me for weeks, seven weeks and one day to be exact, seven weeks and one day of sheer mental torture that had me chucked off my course for not just not doing the work, but for not doing anything, not even getting in touch, and then missing the end of year exams and everything, and it was seven weeks and one day in which I could say no words to you to make it better, to say sorry, to explain why, and even when you did speak to me when you came chapping at my door at ten past two on a Sunday afternoon and put your arms around me and kissed me, I didn't know what to say except 'I love you, Jean'.

Now I'm sitting looking at your name and my chapped hands all hacks and cuts – the cuts from Bernie letting me have a go at preparing some stuff for him because he says being a dishwasher'll not just fuck my hands up and give me a sore fucking back and neck – you know how Bernie talks, the king of the expletives – and think the world is framed by a pair of fucking net curtains, it'll also keep me a pauper, the lowest of the low in the kitchen world so I better learn some other fucking skills and stop being a fucking sud bastard – I think that was his attempt at humour – so now I peel some stuff and chop some stuff and mix some stuff and enjoy it, and big Bernie actually quietens down and stops swearing when he's teaching me the things he's spent years learning, practising and perfecting himself. Then I start to like him, and think he's not such a bad guy, then he'll spit in someone's soup he doesn't like, usually those guys from the council offices, the ones from down south, then I hate him again.

Anyway, I'm sitting here, on the step, fag in right hand, mug of coffee, JEAN on my fair fucked hand, trying to find the words to say what I need to say to you, trying to find the words that convey what I feel. Not just the 'I love you' that says fuck all when it comes out my mouth because I want to say so much more but makes me cry when you say it the way you say it. That's all you have to say to me – 'I love you' – and I know. But what I want to say to you is more than that. I want to tell you I can't exist without you but it sounds like something off a card in the newsagents, even though it's true. I want to tell you you mean everything to me but I could be some guy on the telly handing over a box of gold-wrapped chocolates. And it's the same with all the other phrases that come to mind but have lost their power through overuse, indiscriminate use, like 'have a nice day' in America.

And I'm trying to find the words now because I haven't done anything wrong or upset you in anyway. I don't have to try and placate you or pacify you nor seek forgiveness nor redemption. I'm not, at this particular time, a supplicant. I just want to tell you, that's all. With all the crap in the background from the prima donnas and the deranged and the near suicidal, and my hands hacked and chapped and paining me like fuck and the thought of spending the rest of the summer with that lot making me laugh, really laugh, cause you know what they say, yes, you'll cry if you don't, and I remember last summer and the sunshine that broke the all comers' record – your joke, remember – and the place was packed from morning till night and we made huge batches of vanilla and whisky ice cream from a mix you found at the wholesalers, adding dollops of cheap whisky as we saw fit and passing it off as an old family recipe, calling it 'Bonetti's Inverlochy Whisky Ice Cream' after your grandfather who came over to Scotland to escape Mussolini and his Facisti, as that other Jean calls them, and you said you got your red hair from the woman he married who came from Inverlochty which is near Auchterteuch and not on any map because of its remoteness and in fact there's only half a dozen houses there and they're not worth the seeing and there's no particular landmark nearby, it's just a wee nondescript place tucked away out the road. Kenny sure loved you for that one and we made enough out of that to have that winter holiday in the sun, my first time on a plane and keeching myself like the big fearty I am and you put your arm round me and pulled me close and kissed me on the head and whispered in my ear 'I love you', and those words said everything.

Gordon Kennedy

PASSION

one image, endlessly
of nervous disembodied hands
a circle, dicing
for the garments of the God:
the earth the tree the ragged sky

i watch them strip the body
hear the helix of the drill sing madly
as the hill's great side runs blood;
and they have crowned him
with a ring of wood and wire
and they have soaked a reed
in soured rain, and offered it

i see myself
reach out and place my left hand
in the mountain's side:
a perfect fit

Ian McDonough

RAINBOY

Gobbets of slush rise up
from wheels of vehicles abroad
on saturated minor roads
which always aim for the horizon
never towards home.
Mud angels blink their dangerous
pooling eyes, weep puddles
just for you. Rabbits stare from holes,
startled for you. Rainboy,
where are you travelling
through all these dreadful nights?

An easterly sews your eyes with stitches,
sighs through the ditches of your memory.

And we, at our dishes and our tea,
among the warm towels
and our certainty,
must watch you blister in your shoes.

Far past the headlamps, framed
against a ghastly sky,
mountains stand like cudgels.
Listen, Rainboy,
can you hear the wolves?
They are singing just for you,
telling that tale
of how you wander through our history
on broken, holy feet.

AN EAST COAST SEAGULL'S HYMN

Praise to the providing floor,
To the absence of mercy
In the salt-stung wind.
Praise the lord for herrings
And Mr Chang's Chop Suey
Which grows in abundance
On Saturday nights.

Praise, God of the small, cold eye
For the tasty high water
Glooping round your harbours.
Thank you for the wooden shells
Spewing fishy vomit in their wake.

Praise to the cruel grain of morning
Picked and ripped as clean as bones.
Praise, above all, for clifftops,
For thermals, feathers to stir
And whip the raw-like Northern air.
We sing to our skeletons, light and tough,
To our oils, our claws, our balls.
Praise, Lord, for the beak
Which pecks right hard, and speaks
Not of what you should do with us,
But of what we will do to you.

Morag McDowell

BEING THERE

'Finally, it was confirmed that Jacques Cousteau suffered a fatal heart attack at his home in Southern France last night. The eighty-three-year-old marine biologist, filmmaker and environmental campaigner achieved worldwide fame and success in the seventies for his groundbreaking underwater films. Now, the weather.' She put the teapot back on the kitchen table and sat down. There was a photograph of him, a recent one taken at an airport somewhere. He didn't look like Jacques Cousteau, just a frail old man with his hand held up to his face and a younger wife beside him smiling for the cameras. She wished they hadn't shown him like that for she remembered him in his films, grey-haired but lean and tanned and always framed against a sky so blue it seemed unreal. She'd been eight or nine years old and even now, thirty years later, she could remember the name of the boat. The *Calipso*. Someone knocked on the door.

She checked through the spy hole then opened it, surprised at the way he was dressed. The only suits that ventured up Hawthorn Avenue more or less unmolested were the Garda, the loan sharks and the men from the cable TV company.

'Is Ger in?'

She shook her head.

'I'd like to talk to him if he's in.'

'Well he's not.'

The wind blew hard and a wave of rain and sleet rolled down Hawthorn Walk catching him on one side, soaking his face and lifting up the back of his nice wool coat. He didn't seem to notice but stood there, legs planted wide apart, thickset body bursting with polite aggression.

'Will you give him a message?'

'Depends what the message is.'

He blinked slowly.

'Will you give him a message?' She nodded.

'Ger should keep his appointments. Andy was sorry not to see him last night. He's got till 4 o'clock this afternoon.'

She'd been expecting something like this. She kept her face calm and said steadily,

'What in the name of God are you talking about?'

His eyes watched her from dark wrinkled recesses and his heavy jowls creased into a smile.

'You just make sure he gets that, missus.'

He turned and crossed the road. Within seconds a dark blue Mercedes appeared from round the corner and pulled up beside him. As soon as he got in, the car did a U-turn then sped off in the direction of town and she was back sitting in the living room, though she couldn't remember getting there.

'Isn't it always, Mam?'

They were showing a clip of two divers exploring the depths of some faraway ocean. They held underwater flares and clouds of green smoke spluttered around them then billowed upwards. The camera followed it to the sun-dappled surface then swept down again to focus on one of the divers who had become a small speck merging with the blackness. She remembered the clip, or something like it, from years ago. They'd watched all this sort of stuff avidly on their first colour TV, bought courtesy of Dad's redundancy payment. They'd sit with the lights off, mouths agape, basking in the blue ocean light that played across the living-room walls and their pale winter faces, knowing instinctively what it would feel like to be under that white-hot Mediterranean sun. Like her dad had said at the time, it was almost as good as being there.

Ger hadn't been back for two nights. He was forever disappearing off, going to parties, clubs, a different girl in every bar. She was always fielding phone calls from them. 'Is Ger there? Tell him Shona called.'

'Is Ger back yet? Tell him Mary'll see him at Madigans at eight.'

He was twenty-two years old after all and good-looking. He'd come in drunk late at night, full of jokes and stories and with such a smile and warmth that she didn't mind getting up out of the armchair where she'd been dozing off over the late film and making him sandwiches or toasted cheese. He'd give her a hug and say,

'Yer the best, Mam, really ye are,' and she'd say,

'Watch it.'

Looking back, she realised he'd been a bit jumpy when he'd gone out on Saturday. If Ger had gone AWOL in the past she'd have called Orla for her son Denis had been his pal from schooldays. He was bright like Ger, could have gone to college, but there were too many other things out there that he liked.

On his eighteenth birthday Denny became an entrepreneur or
that's what Orla called it. By the time he was twenty-one he
was travelling up and down to Belfast and London in a brand
new BMW. He moved Orla out of Darndale, bought her a little
terraced house and she couldn't see that it was odd for him to
be pulling in that sort of money so quickly. It was legitimate
business, Orla said, right up to the night three months ago
when she'd found him in his room lying on his bed peaceful as
though he were sleeping but with his eyes wide open and a
bullet hole in his forehead. They'd kept pulling Ger in at first
to help with the murder inquiry, but he didn't know anything.
He'd been at a party that night. She'd asked him at the time,
    'Was it money?' Ger had shrugged,
    'Isn't it always, Mam?'
    They hadn't found the killer. Orla wouldn't answer her
door and whenever she phoned and said,
    'Orla, it's Susan,' she'd slam the receiver down.
    It was probably the same gangsters looking for Ger.
Whether it was the boys from the North or the boys from club
land, guns or smack, it was all the same round here. She was
angry at Ger, but she switched the TV off and went upstairs
anyway to her bedroom and the top shelf of her wardrobe
where she kept a box full of documents, among which was a
deposit book from the Irish Permanent. Ger didn't know about
it, but she'd had it for years. It was only a few thousand
pounds, scraped off part-time jobs and bits of cash Ger had
given her that she didn't like using for she never knew where it
came from. She'd put it all away with the vague idea of going
to see her sister in England, who'd done well – had a husband
and a nice house in a place near London called Potters Bar.
Mona had been pestering her for years to come and visit but
she'd put it off, scared of looking like the poor relation she was
and now Ger was more important. She got the box down and
started to pick through its contents.
    There were some photos of Ger as a baby and one of her
and Orla standing in a Dublin street at night-time, their smiling
faces bleached and ghostly in the camera flash and visible above
their heads a sign for McGonagles night-club. They'd gone there
every Friday and Saturday night, flirting with the doorman who
came from Darndale and knew they were only sixteen but let
them in anyway so they could spend the night drinking snake-
bites, bumping and grinding to Frankie Goes to Hollywood

then chilling out in the video rooms. She'd met Ger's father there. She could still see his face, smiling, relaxed eyes shut listening to the music, while motes of light from the glitter balls swam across his face like silver fishes. It was a strange way to remember him, like a pattern of lights and shadows, not a real person. She didn't even have a photo of him, just this one of her and Orla, the girls, out having a good time. She put the photo back in the box and lifted out a leaflet that was going yellow at the corners. It said on the front in fading typescript 'Careers in Marine Biology'. At school when the teacher had asked them what they'd like to do when they grew up, she'd said,

'I want to be like Jacques Cousteau, you know, go diving in the ocean and make films about sharks and stuff.'

The teacher had held up her hand to stifle the laughter then said,

'Is that so, Susan? Perhaps you could start with fungi at Dingle Harbour.'

She laughed out loud, folded it, unfolded it, folded it again then put it back. There was an unused ferry ticket from Dublin to Liverpool and folded around it a scrap of paper with an address and an appointment time. She'd been at the North Wall ferry terminal, ready to go, but she'd had this picture in her head she couldn't get rid of – something bobbing about inside her with unformed ears like gills and a small spine like a tail and she'd turned around and got the bus back home. And then there was Ger's birth certificate, as though he was the only thing that had happened to her since she was seventeen. She picked up the deposit book and went downstairs.

She got a fright when she saw him lying on the sofa, deadly still, eyes staring up at the ceiling, then, when she realised he was just hung over, she threw the deposit book down on the table in anger.

'Where the feck do you think you've been?'

She didn't wait for an answer, but stamped into the kitchen and began putting the kettle on and getting some bacon out of the fridge for his breakfast then, realising what she was doing, stopped and went back into the living-room. He smiled at her,

'Sorry, Mam. I was going to call you but this thing's busted.' He held up a mobile phone.

'It's not the only thing that'll be busted if you don't get up off yer arse and tell me what you've been up to. Come on.' He stood up, came over to the table and sat down meekly.

'What are you upset about?'

'I'm not upset. Somebody called this morning, looking for you.'

He smiled at her. She said grimly,

'Not a girl.'

His eyes shot open in mock surprise,

'Not a girl?'

'No. A man in a suit.'

He shook his head,

'When will they leave me alone?'

'It sounded as though they wanted something before they'd leave you alone.'

'Oh they want something all right – me banged up in the 'joy for twenty years.'

'What are you talking about?'

'Mountjoy, Mam, Mountjoy prison.'

'I know what the 'joy is, you eejit. I mean why would you go there?'

He picked up the remote control and switched the TV back on.

'Your old pal Orla's been telling tales about me.'

'What sort of tales?'

'That Denny and me had the same contacts, that I owed money...'

He shrugged and flicked through the channels. She saw on the screen the man himself, standing at the helm of the *Calipso* as it sped through the water.

'So what? You were his friend. And you were out with Marie the night it happened.'

He nodded.

'You were, weren't you?'

'Sure.'

'So why are they on at you?'

'Because I had a key to his house. Because there wasn't a break-in.' She cut in and finished it for him,

'Because somebody just walked in the door and they said it was somebody he knew and trusted for he was just lying there, relaxed, like as though he'd been chatting.'

He watched the TV screen, his face blank and passive. She said,

'Ger...'

'I didn't do it, Mam.'

'But you know who did?'

He didn't answer or look at her. She said,

'How did they get in the house?'

A deep voice with a strong French accent said,

'They have dived into the trench now, but we can still track them...'

She wanted him to say something, jump up, give her a hug and ask her for a bacon sandwich, but there was just the blip-blip of the sonar. She stood up.

'It wasn't the Garda this morning. It was a friend of Andy's.'

She went into the kitchen so she didn't have to see the look of relief on his face and made some tea. When she brought it in he was flicking through the bank deposit book. He put it down and looked humbly at the mug she dumped roughly on the table.

'Thanks, Mam.'

He sipped it then said,

'I didn't know you had money in the bank.'

'Well, there you go.'

'I do owe Andy some money.'

'I know. Go to the Garda. Tell them the truth – about every-thing.'

He looked back at the television screen as though he hadn't heard,

'Hey, will ye look at that?'

On an ocean floor somewhere, pale transparent creatures crawled across rocks and shiny paper-thin fish swam blindly past the camera. She said again,

'Go to the Garda, Ger...'

He kept watching the TV.

'I can't, Mam.'

'Why not?'

'It's too complicated to explain. I could pay off Andy though, if I had a little loan.'

'Pay him off for how long?'

He shrugged.

She got her coat from the hallway, lifted the deposit book from the table and put it in her handbag. He looked up at her hopefully. She said,

'You can't pay off Andy. You can never pay off that sort. Come on and we'll go to the station.'

She ruffled his hair with her fingers.

'I'll give you the money if you use it to get away, start somewhere else. There's Mona in London. There's Europe – Germany, France, Italy. Just think of what you could do, Ger.'

The announcer said,

'That film was broadcast in place of the scheduled programme as a tribute to Jacques Cousteau.'

He jerked his head away from her then started to shake it, a bewildered look on his face, flicking through the channels, his fingers jabbing the buttons on the remote until he stopped on MTV.

'Who the fuck is Jacques Cousteau?'

All the time she'd been queuing at the bank and waiting for the girl to close the account she'd thought about him sitting there waiting for her then standing to attention for a photograph in his uniform on his first day at school. On the bus she'd thought of those nights at McGonagles with Orla then at the ferry terminal it was Ger again, when he was just born, plump and slick with amniotic fluid, eyes shut tight, arms waving and small fists curling and uncurling like sea anemones. It was strange thinking of him as a dead man. It made two deaths in the one day. Or maybe not, maybe he would sort it out with Andy, but sooner or later.

'Are you okay, madam?' A man in the ferry terminal uniform was touching her arm. She wiped her eyes.

'I'm fine thank you.'

And she was fine, she told herself, as she shuffled along with the rest of the queue to the gangway. She had ten thousand pounds in fifties in her handbag and a sister in Potters Bar. She was going over the water.

Suzanne McGruther

SKIN DEEP

'Get an eyeful of that, honeybee, those red skins have got themselves a white buffalo,' says my dear husband Eddie as he holds the petrol-pump shakily at his hip. It's a poor tired-looking beast with big mournful eyes, nuzzling the wire fence and rocking the tied-on sign that reads *Feed The Amazing White Buffalo Only $5.*

'Well would you believe that,' I tell Eddie. 'I haven't seen a white buffalo since the Eaton Town Christmas carnival of 1948 when I was crowned Donut Queen and you proposed to me outside Hal's diner. They had a float made from chicken wire and tissue paper and the white buffalo sat on top with a red ribbon around his neck and all the children oohed and aahed. Remember, sweet-pea?'

Eddie glances away, absorbed in staring at some of the Indian boys hanging around outside the reservation gas station. He hasn't been the same since he turned seventy which is really a darn good age for a man and don't I know how lucky I am that he's still got the engine running in there. Still plays golf down at Ten Trees, zipping around on those cute little golf carts. And now he's driving the Infinity again after his knee operation, thank the Lord, although that young Doctor Bradley says he really has to get the weight off which means no candy, soda pop, beer or those lovely itsy-witsy cinnamon cream puff cakes I make that he loves so much. Poor Eddie has the patience of a saint and a half as Momma used to say. May God rest her soul. I know I shouldn't complain about these trips onto the reservation when it's such a disgrace the Government putting up the price of gas, it just holds us over such a barrel; it's not as if we can just stop driving. Eddie always comes out on Sundays to get cheap gas from out on the reservation but I can't say I like it. I'll thole it if that's what my Eddie wants but I can't say I like coming down here at dusk and seeing these Indians with their poor shacks for houses and all they do is sit around all day and drink and not one earning a decent penny.

'Stay in the car, Mabel-pie. This is Injun territory,' says Eddie, wiping his shiny head with his cuff, going inside to pay for the gas. I turn on the CD player with one hand and let the other dangle out of the car windowsill to catch some breeze, cos, gosh, it must have been well into the nineties today and it's hot even this evening by Oklahoma standards. Ah, there now, that lovely Jule Styne and Sammy Cahn song. *You sigh the song begins, you speak and I hear violins, It's magic.* Eddie and I used to hear this on the wireless and be humming it all the way to the American Legion where they used to give out free bubble gum while you watched the movie. We went to see *The Lady from Shanghai* five weekends in a row. *The stars desert the skies and rush to nestle in your eyes, it's magic.* Oh I was so young and lovely then, and I put cold cream on my face every night, and my arms were smooth and white. Not like these bony liver-spotted things – how can that be me? – it's just not me, not really, not inside. Folk just don't understand that I'm still that young girl, Miss Donut Queen 1948 in my bathing suit and high heels with the twenty-two-and-a-half-inch waist-line of Vivienne Leigh. And Eddie may be all whitewashed out and a little paunchy in his cream trousers, and he may be bald under his leather cowboy hat, but he's still handsome and slim in my mind, my young suitor! How he used to make me laugh. *Without a golden wand or mystic charms, fantastic things begin when I am in your arms, it's magic.* Oh my, one of those old Indians is coming this way, limping and long-haired and shabby looking, I do hope he won't talk to me. I'll just look straight ahead and not make eye contact.

'My car – is – broke,' the Indian says, slurring his words. 'Can I hitch…a ride? It's up the hill.' He points and I open my mouth to say no, no, we can't do that, and to call for Eddie but the Indian clicks open the back door of the Infinity and slides inside with a lopsided grin. His face is blithe as a child's, but leathery and folded and he is wearing a stained white T-shirt with a picture of a dream-catcher on it. He just gets right into the back seat of the car! Oh God, Eddie, where are you, and why didn't I lock the car like I should have? *When we walk hand in hand, the world becomes a wonderland, it's magic.* Oh thank God here comes Eddie, he'll soon sort out this rogue.

'Hello there, pumpkin,' Eddie says, and peers into the back of the car at the Indian man and seems to look right through him and doesn't say anything just starts up the car and I'm thinking oh please not now Eddie, don't have one of your funny turns. *How else can I explain, these rainbows when there is no rain, it's magic.* I clasp hold of Eddie's shaking hands and he looks at me dreamily and calls me sugarbabe and touches my cheek. I turn my eyes to the rear-view mirror and the Indian is still there, grinning at us with his black eyes and long hair and his rough brown skin, waiting for his ride home.

'Honey,' I say. 'This nice man wants a ride from us and if he just tells us where to go we'll drop him off quick as can be, won't we dear?' I look at Eddie and he smiles back vacantly and lovingly like he does sometimes. It's okay really, though, because he's been like this before and he's still perfectly safe to drive if you point him in the right direction.

'I'm – a black bear. Black. Lakota. My name is Curt-IS,' he says and his lips move quickly and sink back into his face. His eyes keep sliding away from me when I look at him and I can feel the butterflies in my tummy and dear sweet Jesus I didn't even know they could speak English.

'I was. In Vietnam.' He leans forward as if he is sharing a secret, and I can smell his breath. I'm trying not to gag and suddenly all I can think about is the bag of jelly donuts in the back seat.

'That must have been... Would you like a donut?'

'I do NOT want to talk about it,' he shakes his head.

'That's perfectly understandable. Donut?' I shake the bag, 'Real good!'

He takes one out and starts to eat it and his face changes and then he starts to cry.

'They treat us – so bad.' His face crumples like brown paper.

'Who does?'

'The Government.'

Well I guess it's the 'G' word that sets poor Eddie off and he turns round with his cheeks purple and says to the Indian that the *damn* Government have got a lot to answer for, and he's heard about the boys that got lost in the woods, and he's no fool, he knows what's going on. It was in that national park and when they came out, the FBI de-briefed them. 'And d'ya know what those boys saw?' Eddie asks. 'Foreign troops, I tell ya. National parks ain't *owned* by the U.S. They are bio-spheres controlled by the U.N. You guys ain't the only folks who've lost your sovereignty.'

Well, the Indian stops crying and my heart's going pitter patter pitter patter, and I think that if I can just keep smiling and nodding and looking interested like I learned as a young lady from the Tilly Taylor School of Evening Charm, then everything will work out just fine.

'I'll pray for you. For your safe journey home,' the Indian says. He has sugar on his lips.

'That's real nice of you, isn't it, Eddie?' I pause the CD player out of respect, and the Indian closes his eyes and begins to hum and rock back and forth, and then this sound comes from his belly – all guttural and floaty – and not exactly like real music but all in a different language all wheeya hoyah, and it makes my heart slow down and my hands stop shaking.

'Stop here,' he says and I open my eyes and he's ended his singing. Eddie stops the car and for a moment stares out of the window and then he looks at me with a confused expression and then turns and looks at the Indian in the back seat of his Infinity.

'Who the *heck* are you?'

'Please... money... some dollars. Money. For the song,' the Indian mumbles and puts out his hand and his palm is all criss-crossed with long white scars probably from Vietnam I suppose. Right then I feel real sorry for the poor man and start to dig into my purse but just then Eddie lifts his fist and brings it down on the open palm with a slap.

'Git. Git OUT my car,' says Eddie, and his face is turning purple and I can see the veins stick out in his neck and I think oh Lordy I haven't seen him this mad since he took a funny turn and sunk his brand new set of golf clubs in the lake off hole four. The Indian sorta sits back and stares at Eddie and then he spits into his own hand and wipes it on my face and I scream and open the car door and Eddie's shouting obscenities at the Indian. I grab my cheek and wipe like fury and try to take that terrible stain off my skin, and oh Lord what an animal and on my face, I can't take that, it's not right! The smell, the stink. I can't seem to get that Injun spit off and it's making me queasy and I'm suddenly thinking dear sweet Jesus we've been lured out here to this total wilderness to be robbed and scalped and I can just picture Eddie's bald pate and my graying locks hang-ing from a hook on a wall. I bend over and think I'm gonna sick up when two great beams of light come sweeping up the hill and round the bend comes this shiny big car and it draws to a halt and out comes this man. Sure enough, he's an old Indian, as brown and wrinkled as a chestnut, but he's wearing a pin-stripe navy suit and a pocket-watch, and his short hair is oiled and slicked to one side like a man coming to pay a Sunday visit to his bride-to-be. Well, he shuffles over to the Infinity and opens the back door and stares in at that crazy Indian.

'Come on, Curtis, it's time to go home,' he says, and takes that loony Indian by the hand and leads him away as if he's a small child even though the old man himself doesn't even come up to his shoulders. And Curtis goes meek and mild and sits in the back of the other car, and out comes a young girl of maybe twenty or twenty-five with black hair and big brown eyes and skin the colour of milky coffee, and she's wearing a dress that looks as if it's been dyed the colour of the sea.

'I'm Gerald Elk, and this is my new wife Gina,' the old man smiles, showing yellowed and broken teeth.

'Mabel and Eddie Burden from Eaton Town,' I smile at them, in what I hope is a gracious manner. 'How very nice of you to come to our aid, I'm afraid my husband is feeling rather poorly, and I think we're a little lost. Perhaps you could be so kind as to point us in the direction of the gas station, the one where the white buffalo lives – that's where we started.'

'That swindler!' Gina cries, and her face opens up and I see to my horror that her teeth are yellow and broken too, but Mr Elk pats her on the arm.

'The white buffalo is a sacred animal to us. A real Indian would never have one to show off and make money. Joe wants to be an Indian so bad that he grows his hair long and wears beads around his neck. All because the Government will give him benefits.'

'*Damn* the government...' Eddie calls from the car and I rush over and put a hand on his arm and tell him he needs to take the weight off that knee and he does just as I say, like a good boy, and sits back in the car.

'You should be careful,' Mr Elk says. 'They don't like whites here. It means trouble, and there's been a lot of trouble here. A lot of fighting and trouble. Not a month ago the elders got together and decided that someone had to do something to stop the violence. One of our elders, a very respected and good old man, went into a bar where the whites drank. Maybe they got into an argument with him. Maybe they thought he was funny. All I know is that those men stripped that old man naked, pushed the music as loud as it would go, and stomped on him, whooping and yelling in a white war dance until he was broken. Do you understand, lady? You should leave the reservation.'

It's dark and the stars are little cobwebs up above. I nod to Mr Elk and get in the car and pat Eddie's knee and he looks at me and I wonder if he really sees me as he starts up the engine and backs down the hill.

'Sugarbean, do you know where you're going?' I ask Eddie, and he takes my hand and smiles at me like he used to on carnival days. The road is rough and bumpy and there are no signposts, only a huge spray of blood fanned across the road. Something has died up here and I don't want to know what, I just shiver to myself and turn on the CD player again and hope that my darling Eddie is safe enough to find the way home.

Why do I tell myself all these things that happen are all really true? When in my heart I know the magic is my love for you.

Rob MacIlleChiar

DUILICH GU BHEIL MI FADALACH –

air mo rathad gu ruige seo
mhothaich mi dhan ghealaich
air a ribeadh
air gathan craoibh-uaithe

SORRY I'M LATE

on my way here
I noticed the moon
entangled
on the hawthorn's barbs

Tony McLean

RULE #4

A cautionary tale on the rules of high rise living.

Rule #1. Don't grass.

Rule #2. Never get in or out of the lift on the floor that you live on.

Rule #3. Unless you're up for the cup, keep yourself to yourself.

If you can't abide by these rules then you shouldn't live in the sky.

Rule #2 is especially important if the foyer and lifts of the building are fitted with security cameras. Cameras monitored twenty-four seven by little green men who go by the name of concierges. Jumped-up jannies with a French-sounding job title that I'm sure makes them feel better about mopping up sick and piss in the aforementioned lifts. 'Quelle domage. Puke dans l'elevator!' Jannies playing I Spy with residents' lives. Jannies who are no better than the rest of us. Worse most of the time. They will happily disobey Rule #1, especially if there's some greasy palm action going down. Not to the police, but to other tenants who don't have the surveillance equipment to play I Spy. Other tenants with a need to know.

So. Fourteen storeys up, middle of the night and I think I'm asleep, but I'm not sure. I feel as though someone's done the old cartoon routine of painting pupils, irises, and lashes onto the outside of my eyelids. I only realise I'd been sleeping when I wake up with a start. I lie a second or two, wondering what's caused it. No noise, then it's **OH YES! OH YES! OH YES! OH YES! OH YES! OH MY GOD YEEEEESSSSS!** from the woman upstairs. I'm lying there on my todd, a year or so since I'd last tried and failed to give it **AFFIRMATIVE BABY!** with anyone. In the last four years she's only ever disturbed me in daylight hours, the daily grind of her Hoover interfering with the picture on the telly, or the trembling of the lightshade in my kitchen as her washing machine shakes, rattles and rolls into action. This is the first nocturnal disturbance though. The noise stops and I don't hear any talking, just two pairs of feet padding back and furret to the toilet.

I stick my napper under the duvet and close my eyes, knowing that I've work at stupid o'clock in the morning and the last thing I need is to be awake all night. Of course, it doesn't work out like that. The wee cogs in my bonce are going bananas thinking about this, that, and the other. Especially the other.

Eventually a dream sequence kicks in and I know it won't be long till I'm safely asleep in the Land of No...

THAT'S ME! THAT'S ME! THAT'S ME! YES JASON! YES! THAT'S ME!

IIIIIIIII'MMMMMMMMMMM W I D E A W A K E !

Again? I look at the alarm; it's only twenty-five minutes later! Christ on a bike! I wanted to shout up that she was faking it, but my impotent rage wouldn't allow it.

I'm awake a wee bit longer this time, the cogs turning faster, gradually getting my mind into the swing.

This happens another three times during the night. That's five in total.

L
E
E
T
S
MAN OF

The alarm hits my ears and I'm lying there listening to the weather when Jesusmaryandjoseph she's away again. My alarm must've woke them and they decided a half six quickie was the order of the day. They must've been bloody red raw.

That day I'm fit for nothing, nearly falling off my ladder and covering the right side of my coupon with emulsion twice.

This carries on all over the Christmas holidays then every Tuesday, Wednesday and Thursday after that. Why never the weekends? I could cope with that. I'd always thought that I could put up with most things, tolerate the intolerable, become accustomed to anything. Not this though. This still keeps me awake, still annoys me, still makes me feel SO BLOODY LONELY. At one point I moved the bed into the living room, but it made no odds. I could hear her giving it laldy in every room in my flat. Surroundsound shagging. It felt as though my life was no longer my own, that I was intruding on them and their wee tryst. Something had to give.

I couldn't go up and complain. Could I? Maybe suggest she wears a gag? No, complaining would end in disaster. It always did. I'd rehearse and rehearse for days before finally plucking up the courage to go up and batter forcefully on her door. I'd know exactly what I wanted to say then the door would swing open and I'd be confronted by something that I hadn't anticipated in my practices.

Wham! A big hairy-knuckled growler of a man asking what my problem was.

Bam! The pair of them answering the door to me naked or kitted out in rubber.

Thank You Mam! She'll answer the door and invite me in for a quick jump of her bones to compensate for my insomnia. As per usual I wouldn't be able to raise as much as a smile.

Complaining to the council wasn't the answer either. They'd just think I was some sad case. Earplugs were no good; I'd miss the alarm at stupid o'clock. No, I'd just have to wait for the inevitable boredom of their relationship to kick in.

A few days later I'm on my way to Springburn, just passing the next door tower block, blue and white police ribbon flapping about all over the place, when I spot the flowers. A Lidl-bought posy tied with a wee yellow ribbon to the railings that yesterday's high-flying junky had bashed into a concertina shape. I just walked past and tried not to look. If I don't see it, it doesn't exist. But, like some huge wart on the face of some BIG BRUISER, I'm drawn to it, can't take my eyes off it. They're nothing, rubbish; they're one seventy-nine tops. No wonder he took up skydiving. Anyway, I stick it in the lost and found at the back of my mind and scoot up to Shevlanes for a session with Italian Paul.

He's in sparkling form, thinks my problem with the folk upstairs getting their jollies is hilarious. He wants to come round and listen just for old time's sake. Remind himself of what life used to be like. Our fun day out gets cut short when a neurotic Linda comes in and tells him she can't find their cat anywhere. I know he wants to smile, but his love for Linda is much greater than his hatred of the moggy so he consoles her with a brandy. Then a couple of punters that should know better go toe-to-toe and fist-to-fist over a taxi. 'It's ma car!' BELT. 'Mine!' THUMP. 'Mine!' BEL... An ambulance is called on our ambience and it's time to call it a day.

On the way back home I'm passing the concertina railings

and I see some sod's swiped the flowers.

I approach my block and get the key fob from my pocket, ready to zap the panel on the door. When I get there some guy's talking into the speaker. 'Aye,' he says. 'It's me.' **Didleydit didleydit didleydit didleydit.** Open Sesame! He pulls the door to and I grab it from him. He looks at me, suspicion tattooed across his forehead. This reaction lets me know he's not local. We'd hold the door open for Auld Nick without batting an eyelid.

While we're waiting for the lift to come down he unzips his jacket and there they are. Flowers that once belonged to a sky-diver, yellow ribbon and all. I think about saying something but it might just be some unfortunate coincidence. Aye right. I pass comment on his jacket instead, the drink making me brave. 'Good warm jacket that, mate, get it up the Cawder?' I say this with a smile on my chops but his frown and apeman grunt just confirm to me his alien status on the scheme.

His jacket's a bright red **North Face** with the hood. Every household within a square mile of the Cawder has one hanging about on a coat hook. I've got one. In the summer some chancer was selling them, tenner a pop. Course, in the summer they weren't needed, but come the first cold day of autumn and out they came. It looked like an audition for the Greenland Butlins. The very next day bright red **North Face** jackets were extinct. Couldn't see one anywhere.

The lift comes and we get in in silence. He presses 15 so I don't bother. I'm wondering whether he's the Man of Steel, old Duracell Jason. The lift shunts to 15 and he shuffles out first. I saunter behind, curious to see if he goes to the flat directly above mine. Bingo. He does a right and makes a beeline straight for it. I pass him waiting at the door, stolen flowers clutched proudly to his chest. As I'm almost at the back stairs I hear her answer the door. It's all 'Oh they're lovely' and 'Aren't you a sweet-heart?' Aren't you a grave-robbing bastard might've been more appropriate, but it wasn't my business.

I'm only in the door five minutes when they're at it again. Banging away like bunnies thanks to a dead man's flowers. I stick on a CD really loud in the hope that it'll drown them out.

Life goes on and I'm sure my lack of sleep is ageing me pre-maturely. All through tea and lunch breaks I'm spark out. Some days fit for nothing, it's as if my body's been sent into warp-speed deterioration. The only thing to do was bite the bullet, make up some excuse and ask the council for a transfer quick smart.

I make an appointment at the health centre and don't wash or shave for a couple of days prior to it. The doctor takes one look at me. 'Depression,' I tell him. 'Why?' he asks. 'Altitude sickness,' comes the reply. Bish Bosh! Panel line to take down the council in the morning with the rent, get them to sort out the necessary paperwork.

I'm just heading into the foyer of my block, bright red **North Face** jacket on cause it was Baltic, hood up cause it was pissing, when something on the ground catches the attention of my beady. I crouch down, hood still up, and scrutinise it. It's brown, but it's not a turd. I pick it up, sniff, and realise that I've simultaneously hit the jackpot *and* stepped into the danger zone. It's at least an ounce of dope! Just lying there waiting for little old me. I stuff it deep in my pocket and head for the lift. All the while the hood stays up, steadfastly hiding my unshaven face from the curious concierges and their talkative tongues.

I knew exactly who it belonged to, and had a fair idea what he'd do to me if he found out I had it. Blond Gary. Carries his stash about the scheme in a Safeway's carrier that's obviously sprung a leak. I'd had a visit from him Christmas Eve. He was dashing around like some dope-dealing Santa, making sure all the good little girls and boys were safely sorted before midnight. The situation could get tricky. He's well connected, wired to the moon in fact. Cross him and you'll soon know all about it.

The lift comes and I get in with the head down. My greedy genes are telling me to press 14 and get a spliff on the go pronto. But, my sensible genes are getting more devious by the second. I press 15, back to the camera, hood still up. If the jumped-up jannies are watching there's only one bloke on the scheme been seen wearing a red **North Face** jacket recently. The love machine that is Jason. If they've been paying attention they'll know he gets off at 15. If they're really thorough they'll've spied him buzzing her number through the camera in the foyer. So, they spy me picking up a lump of blow wearing the red jacket. 2 + 2 = 5. Result.

I get out at 15, do a right as if going to the flat directly above mine, but walk round the landing to the back stairs. I bomb down and in no time at all I'm stoned stupid and staring at the contents of my fridge.

Midnight. I'm in bed, images flying through my mind at

such a rate that I just can't keep up. Then it starts from upstairs, the squeaking of the bedsprings and the banging of the headboard against the wall. My wee images are shattered into a million technicolour pieces of shrapnel. Couple of minutes later it's **oh yes Jason! Oh yes! Oh Ye...**

Bang!   Bang!   Bang!

Somebody's hammering big time on their door. 'Who the h...?' I hear her scream. Then there's padding to the door.

Bang!   Bang!   Bang!

Relentless.

Bang!   Bang!   Bang!

I hear a click of the lock then all hell seems to break loose. Screams of 'Where's ma fuckin dope?' Cries of 'I don't know what ye're talkin about.' Pleas of 'Leave him alone, he's done nothing.'

I'm quaking under my quilt. Sounds as though a heavy-duty doin's about to go down. The wee technicolour pieces of shrapnel have re-formed in my mind's eye and I can visualise everything that's happening upstairs. I'm out of bed cricking my good ear to the ceiling so that I don't miss a word.

'Put him oot the windae!' I hear Gary scream. I instantly get the image of wired to the moon Gary and his equally eccentric chums dangling the naked Man of Steel from the 15th floor. This was better than any cable channel.

She starts screaming blue murder. 'What dope? What've you been up to, Jason? After all I went through with my brother! Leave him! Leave him!'

'Oot the windae!'

'Stop it! Stop it! I can give you money!' she squeals.

It quietens down to low moaning and I can't make out anything that's being said. Considering the size of the lump in question the poor dear's going to have to shell out at least eighty squidily.

A minute or so later there's another **Bang!** of the door upstairs and my mind's eye tells me that Gary and his minders are gone. There's a couple of seconds' silence before another explosion.

'DON'T YOU TOUCH ME! DON'T YOU DARE COME
NEAR ME!'

I don't get anything else that's said until,

'GET OUT! I NEVER WANT TO SEE YOU AGAIN!'

A few minutes pass then there's another slamming of the
door. All at once there's a foggy silence covers my ears and I'm
smiling like the cat that's got the skooshy cream. I know that
the only noises I'll be hearing for a while will be the growling
of her Hoover and the whirring of her washing machine. I feel
a good night's sleep coming on.

Before I drop off I should tell you **Rule #4**. Don't get caught.

Anne MacLeod

JOHN DEPP IS BIG LEGGY

Isn't loneliness the bigger sin? See, life is like this fancy camera.

What you get is not necessarily what you hoped you saw through the computerised viewfinder; and memory confuses, adding colour and emotion, skewing perspective. The picture always lies. So.

You got it. I'm not perfect.

I could tell you more; I could tell you that my favourite actor, Johnny Depp, in one of my favourite films, *Ed Wood*, lies sleepless in bed next to his girlfriend... she doesn't know he wears all her angora sweaters, doesn't know she's for the chop... *Perhaps*, he says, *I just don't got it*. Those eyes. Did you see *Benny and Joon*? *Of course you got it, honey*, she soothes. *Now go to sleep*. He doesn't. In the script he really don't got it, except, he don't got it so bad he becomes cult. In angora.

I don't want to be cult in angora. I don't want any part of don't got it. I wouldn't mind being Johnny Depp's girl even when the next scene says I'm sacked. I'd throw the saucepans at him, don't worry, like the script says. I would never know when he was acting, that would be the trouble.

Don Juan de Culbokie. Who could resist?

In the movie of my life, I'd be widescreen. The pitch? That's not so certain.

I know what it wouldn't be. Not *Ed Wood*, not *Braveheart*. Not *Over the Rainbow* (I mean the *Wizard of Oz*, turkey). Not *Little Women*. Not *Sex, Lies and Videotape*, though I liked that film, I really did. James Spader. Another *actor*. A face you could pour any emotion into and still it would be the character, you know? Not as lovable as Johnny, a more sinister blankness. I've never really trusted him since *Pretty in Pink*, but hey, *Sex, Lies and Videotape*, that was something.

I suppose it would have to be *Scissorhands* meets *Casablanca*. (Don't you just love Bergman even when she's not playing a nun?) Story of my life. People love *Casablanca*. I love *Casablanca*, though they all live unhappily ever after. Drinking too much. It gets them through the day.

My movie is a romance, quest movie too, part-detective. Science fiction. Mythological. Filmed in Technicolor as well as black and white, so the joy, the last ounce of emotion, no matter how economically rendered, will lift you to a new plane of psychic well-being, or drop you in the depths of confusion. We're going for the general audience, not film-house, though we will of course seek public as well as industry backing... if Tracy Emin's bed (is that how you spell Emin?) can do it, why not the darkest secrets of my movie life? It will be called *This... my Life*. Good, eh? Shades of *This Life*, shades of *This is Your Life*, shades of *Big Brother*, though this will be film, and not constructed non-documentary. No Nasty Nick. I've scripted the whole project, had development funding.

So.

Are you sitting comfortably?

I should warn you the dialogue is in Gaelic (we've had Gaelic funding too. Subtitles in English and Doric. If you speak Lallans you'll just have to translate for yourselves). The screen will be divided in four, your attention subtly drawn towards the active frame by the use of sea and mountain imagery. You'll get it, don't worry.

First Screen – Top Left

It is midnight, on a white, deserted beach. High summer. The sky is as bright as early dawn, not dark enough for stars. The camera plays round the high sandstone cliffs, settles on the restless sea, panning the receding tide; the endless crying of the waves is merged with the occasional screaming of a seagull, and gentle breathing. You become more and more conscious of the gentle breathing, as if you're the camera, and you are running.

The camera now picks up a trail of recent footprints, follows them to slender feet, white, bare legs. A hand reaches down, picks up a key, lays it on rock beside a shimmering tail. Feet and tail merge, become one. A small wind rises, whipping up the inshore waves. The tail splashes, is gone.

At the far end of the beach, in a low white cottage, Johnny Depp sits late over his computer-animated mermaid. Phones his agent in the States. *You really don't got it*, the agent sings from his jacuzzi. *A winner, I don't think. Who in God's name needs another mermaid film?* Johnny Depp looks at his much-loved creation, stretches one hand towards her. Tears gather in those innocent eyes. *No, wait*, he says. *This... is a mermaid with a difference...* The agent, sceptical, flicks his cigar ash over plastic grass. *Oh yeah?* Johnny is standing now. The cottage door has opened silently. *Yes,* he breathes. *A mermaid with a difference. A mermaid...* The agent mops his brow, waves his busty girl away. *A mermaid,* says Johnny, *with wings...* A flurry of pure white feathers wafts across the room. In LA the agent splutters, *What are you on? Mermaids don't got wings, they got tails.* Johnny puts the phone down, moves across the room, stooping to gather the drifted feathers. In LA the agent gasps. His jacuzzi is suddenly a whirling mass of white, white soft stuff. Not snow.

On the shore, two sets of footprints stop suddenly, end in uplift. On the far horizon, a cloud resembles wings. Johnny is flying, flying with his mind alone. No wings. No strings.

The agent in LA grabs the phone. *Get me the Water Department!* All his tropical fish have escaped into the swimming pool. *Gee, Al...* the busty girl says, *get a load of this...* Al gasps. His fish grow wings, fly off into the dusk.

On Johnny's computer we see Al's troubled face... *This is a job for only one man...* The girlfriend takes a deep breath. Her breasts rise and fall. *You don't mean?* Al sighs. *Yeah... The lone sea-ranger...* He spins on his heel and is transformed into a young sea-god with golden curls and white shining mask. A sea-green trident glitters in his hand. He strikes the water in the pool before him, transforming it, dividing the waves, like the Red Sea parting before Moses. He steps into the breach and on to the beach. Finds himself in Johnny's cottage. Dusts a swathe of feathers from the chair.

The lone sea-ranger stretches his hand towards the mouse. (Big music here, the tension almost unbearable) He draws down the Edit menu, selects **Ends**. Clicks on Big Finish. Shakes his head in disbelief as the picture forms before him. A girl with wings and glittering mermaid's tail crosses the setting sun.

Close-up of Johnny and the Mermaid kissing.

And that's the first screen.

The second screen, Top Right, shows the main door of a hospital. An ambulance has just pulled up. Two medics, in green, jump from the front seats, rush to open the back doors: they look anxious. They're in a hurry. A low trolley slides out. Red mattress, with white cotton blankets. The figure strapped on to the trolley becomes slowly visible (we're not playing real-time here), a young dark-haired man is writhing, fitting uncontrollably. We do not see his face.

It's raining. The distant hills are covered in cloud. A few folk in dressing gowns stand outside the hospital, smoking. They show no interest in the ambulance, gaze beyond the rain, into the distance.

The medics wheel the trolley into Accident and Emergency as quickly as they can.

From the trolley patient's POV, we see a blond-haired doctor bending over him, a dark-haired nurse. Their faces are distorted, their voices anxious, echoing. No-one seems to know who the patient is. *Just relax. We'll soon have you comfortable. What's your name? Have you taken anything you shouldn't...?*

He was found at the foot of the cathedral steps, says the medic. *No identification. When we picked him up he was covered in these.* He hands a downy feather to the young consultant.

Flashback to the cathedral steps, the dark head lying at an awkward angle. People gathered round.

Back to the hospital. Accident and Emergency. The consultant shakes her head, watches the doors in the crash-room swing shut behind the trolley. Pushes through. Johnny's face (for it is he) registers great pain, then, suddenly, serenity. His arching back slides flat against the trolley. His eyes close. The nurses' faces fall.

The young policeman standing by the door shakes his head. *Drugs, doc?* The blonde consultant sighs. *Looks like it.*

The crash room is empty. The camera shows drip set hanging empty, ECG wires cast aside, on the floor. Empty syringes. The trolley vacated, the pillow still recording an impression of the boy's head. *Dr Advent!* a nurse cries. *He's gone!* The blonde doctor dashes into the room to find empty blankets filled with soft white feathers. A sudden swirling draught lifts them, in a ghostly outline of the missing lad.

High above the cathedral, a huge winged figure hovers. A dark-haired boy is climbing the sheer front wall, climbing without ropes or safety-devices. High above him we see a huge winged statue smiling. The camera shows the statue's face, the wings, the huge stone fish-like tail.

The blonde consultant stands at the foot of the cathedral frontage. She can see Johnny climbing high above her. She limbers up the fancy stonework round the great central door, looking upwards, breathless, searching for footholds.

Third Screen – Bottom Left

Johnny arrives for work. His Airstream trailer, polished steel, stands out from all the others on location at Big Sands Caravan and Camping Park. A voice off-camera calls out, *Good morning, Mr Depp. How are you this morning?* Johnny waves, opens his trailer door. The mountains to the south are blue against the early morning sky. The wide white beach is empty.

In the caravan, he slumps into a blue reclining chair. Closes his eyes. Does not speak. The make-up girl, without a word, approaches, drapes a blue silk gown across him. Switches on soothing island music. Slowly, almost lovingly, she paints his pale and empty face, using her array of natural colourings: beach-sand white, fish-tail silver-green, mountain blue, heather purple... the camera dancing from the natural object to the skin, the loving, working fingers.

Johnny's face becomes the landscape. Only at the end, as she removes the blue silk wrap, the sky, only then do we catch a glimpse of wings.

Fourth Screen – Bottom Right

A computer VDU fills the screen. ASCO YOUR COMPUTER SUPERMARKET

The camera draws back to show a young girl sitting, registering lists of customers' orders. Me. I print each list, find a trolley, rush round the huge grey warehouse compiling each order, which I then pack, perfectly (I'm most particular about this), in cardboard boxes; I help the driver load his van, go back to the screen. Pick up a new order.

All this happens time and time again. My fingers are sore, cracked. The skin looks almost scaly, shines silver green in the warehouse artificial light.

The computer screen before me fades into a television. Now I am at home, no longer in uniform. My hair hangs round my shoulders. There's a glass of amber liquid in my hand.

I wander round the flat, so empty, so black and white. In the kitchen, a pile of unwashed dishes. In the lounge, a pile of videos, old classics, angel films, Depp. In the bedroom, my unmade bed.

On the TV screen, my own face. *Play it, play it, Sam. Play* **As time goes by.** Sam plays. Rick's face turns into Johnny Depp.

The computer screen blares GOOD MORNING! ASCO THE COMPUTER SUPERMARKET WELCOMES *YOUR*

ORDER. <<<ASK FOR ANYTHING>>> ASCO WILL FIND
IT FOR YOU. I print off lists, piling them beside the key-
board. Begin my first trolley of the day. Cornflakes. Flour.
Tinned salmon on special offer.

A supervisor pops her head around the door. *New driver.
Name of Ed. He may need help... slightly disabled. Be nice.*
She's gone before I answer.

A huge pile of boxes stands waiting by the door when he
finally appears in hair and leathers. He does not speak. Those
scissorhands are going to make the job a little difficult for him.
I look into his eyes. He smiles. *Haven't we met?* I wish we had.
Don't think so.

The screen flickers: TODAY'S SPECIAL OFFER – FREE
WITH EACH ORDER – MERMAID STEAKS. *What's in
these tins?* says Ed, balancing one between his blades. His
movements are so delicate... even the paper on the tin remains
intact. *Farmed salmon, I should think.* I smile back into those
eyes. *Wingfield are one of the oldest salmon farming outfits.* He
shrugs. *Odd name.*

I know. I smile again. *They used to be in chickens. Some
imaginations though. Who could ever farm mermaids? They
don't exist.*

Johnny sighs. *Who would want to eat them? I knew a
mermaid once*, he says. *With wings.*

Cut to my bedroom. The open wardrobe. Focus on the
tail, the wings.

The midnight beach. I am the mermaid with the key; I
unlock the metal tank a hundred metres offshore. Mermaids
spill everywhere, strike out across the waves. One or two, not
more, take wing. Johnny, flying overhead, is waiting for me.

Cut to Big Finish. As Screen One.

The credits roll, Hayzee Fantayzee sing *John Depp is Big
Leggy*. I've always liked that song, but not John Wayne, the guy
they sang it for. On reflection, maybe we ought to change the title
– *Mermaid Stakes?* Or even *Local Heroine?* I just don't know.

See, there is, in all our lives, this celtic knot of timing. Or
perhaps it's more an undecidability... you get what you pay
for; you pay for all your choices, and the hard part – the earth-
moving-finger-licking-shape-shifting-slainte-mhor crappest
part of all – is that time does not reveal, will never let you see,

the full range of possibilities at the moment when you actually have to *choose.*

A bit like ASCO. You see what's on the menu offered. You never know what's coming next week, what you would be better waiting for. And you type your order in, and they leave it at your door, and you're stuck with it. You live alone and speak to no-one, just the grey-white screen, electrons dancing.

Loneliness. The biggest sin of all.

Hugh McMillan

JOE BAKER'S BOOTS

Douglas MacTaggart walked to school on Monday morning, his shoulders hunched. As usual, he expected to be the subject of good-natured insults and downright abuse from his so-called friends after Hibs' latest defeat. He shook his head. It wasn't easy supporting Hibernian FC, especially not now, long after the glory days of the '70s, when they were propping up the foot of the Premier League and doomed, short of a miracle, for relegation. They'd just been beaten 5-0 by St Johnstone, which was the footballing equivalent of being beaten up by a sheep. As Dougie lived in Drumsleet, which considered itself in foot-balling terms in the west of Scotland, most of his fellow pupils supported one or other of the Glasgow giants, most being fans of Glasgow Rangers, especially since they'd won the European Champions' League last season, beating Manchester United in Extra Time. Rangers had then gone on to sign Rafael Domingo Sanchez, the world's most expensive and gifted footballer, from Juventus for thirty-five million quid. He'd scored five goals in his first game, ironically against St Johnstone, the team that had just given Hibs such a drubbing.

Dougie could imagine the witticisms that would be flung at him as soon as he went in the school gates. 'How are Hibsnil getting on?' the Gimp would ask. The Gimp was no mental giant and he thought the Hibsnil joke was one of the best and most amazing bits of wit ever invented. 'Oh I thought Hibsnil was their name,' he would say, rubbing his forehead inno-cently, 'I've heard it on the telly that often I thought it was their name.' Dougie shouldered his bag, tightened his Pride of Leith scarf and moved up the school steps. He could see his friends gathered at the top, where the snow had been swept away by the jannies. He braced himself for the first piece of abuse, which arrived on cue, a milli-second later.

'I know, I know,' said Dougie through gritted teeth. He shrugged and tried to smile, but he was anything but happy, especially since, the following Sunday, two days before Christmas, Rangers, Rafael Domingo Sanchez and all, were due to take on Hibs at Ibrox Park. Dougie couldn't begin to imagine what would happen. Well he could, really. Hibs would be beaten 38-0 or something like that, and he would have to run away to sea or commit suicide, or murder more like. The Gimp would say Hibsnil once too often and Dougie would snap, turning into a wild animal and strangling him. Life imprisonment would be a relief to the average Hibs fan, though knowing his luck the inmates would find out and tap Hibsnil all night in Morse code on the heating pipes.

'The trouble is,' he was patiently explaining to his pal Billy at interval, 'the trouble is...' 'They're complete crap,' interrupted Billy, chewing at his Twix. Dougie was about to launch into some complicated analysis of tactics and strategy and the 4-2-2-2 system, but Billy was absolutely right. The basic problem was that they were, indeed, crap. They had sold their last really good players, Russel Latapy and Kenny Miller, last season and had bought instead some Guatemalan reject called Jesus Hosanna Stevenson who'd been hospitalised after his first game – a league cup tie against Clydebank at Boghead – after suffering from exposure on the right wing. And now they were about to face Rangers and the brilliant Rafael Domingo Sanchez, who was going out with Ginger Spice and had scored the winning goal for Brazil in the last World Cup Final. It was the nightmare scenario. Dougie would become the laughing stock of 3N1. And it was tough enough, as any fourteen-year-old could tell you, striking the right attitude, the right balance between coolness and popularity, between fashionable disdain and care for what folk, even teachers, thought of you. And it was a jungle out there. Teachers didn't know the half of it. They thought that if there was some kind of order in their classes, everything was great. They didn't realise it was a jungle in school, in that respect like any other similar institution like prisons or madhouses. It was the inmates that set the real rules. Dougie had always got on pretty well, admittedly. He was tall for his age, no pushover, had a brain and was as street wise as a teenager from south-west Scotland could be. He was pretty good looking in a rangey blond mop-top kind of way, too, but this Hibs business was beginning to set him apart. It was like a deformity, like having a giant boil on his forehead, or a hump on his back, or a note to let him out to the toilet. A few times he'd thought about giving it all up, but blue didn't suit him. Besides, he was proud to be different, to follow Hibs and their stupid sloping pitch, and to have huddled in the sleet at Fir Park, Dens, Pittodrie, Firhill, Cappielow and other arctic venues the length and breadth of Scotland. He was a Hibs man.

Always was, always would be, and for the hundred vacant, incredulous looks he got when he said it, there was always the company of other die-hards in the same boat, people who didn't need success or big-name players to earn support but who felt it in their hearts. Like his dad, though he had had the fortune to see them in their glory days. 'And up strode Joe Baker,' he would sing after a pint or two, 'and scored a fine goal, and Tynecastle erupted in green white and gold!'

None of this helped him in Drumsleet Academy, however, where the Gimp was organising more and more opinion against him, building up the match on Sunday to be a real grudge affair. The Gimp was about six feet wide with no neck, which made him a real player in events and though he and Dougie had never come to blows, they had an uneasy relationship, made more so by the problem of Catherine Murdoch, a statuesque black-haired girl who had taken a shine to Dougie but whom the Gimp obviously fancied, in his troll-like way. 'I wouldn't like to be in your shoes on Monday,' said Billy helpfully. Dougie shrugged, finished off his Mars Bar and went up the stairs to Modern Studies.

At lunchtime, things degenerated. They were in their Register Room, sitting about with Catherine and her friends when the Gimp waddled in. 'What about Hibsnil this Sunday then. You going to the game?' Dougie nodded. The Gimp sat down beside Catherine, took one of her Maltesers and stuffed it in his mouth. He winked at her. 'My dad knows Sanchez, you know.' The Gimp's dad was big in the construction industry and had bought shares in Rangers back in Walter Smith's day. The Gimp was always flaunting this knowledge in front of people, especially girls. 'Really?' said Catherine, her eyes wide open. She was wearing a Rafael Domingo Sanchez T-shirt, showing on the front his handsome tanned face and on the back the spectacular overhead kick that had won the World Club Championship for Rangers in October. 'Yea,' said the Gimp, 'meets him regularly. Invited him down here, in fact.' The Gimp now had an adoring circle of friends of both sexes. 'You could maybe meet him.' 'Could we?' asked Catherine. Her mouth couldn't have got much wider, without dropping to the floor. The Gimp nodded modestly, as though he had the influence to pull this off. 'Rafael is so cool,' breathed Catherine. 'Immense,' agreed one of the others.

Looking back later, Dougie could never understand why he

had said it, but as if from a great distance he heard the muscles of his mouth move and a voice – it was his, he knew – say, 'He's not as good as Jesus Hosanna Stevenson.' There was a stunned silence, then the expected avalanche of derision. 'What?' cried the Gimp, sensing blood in the war against Dougie, 'that reject? Better than the captain of Brazil?' Dougie thought of poor Jesus Hosanna Stevenson being stretchered off at Boghead, stiff as a board. The Gimp was laughing now, staring with mock incredulity at the others who were all joining in, apart from Catherine and Billy who were looking away in embarrassment. 'Yes,' said Dougie, recklessly. 'He's about to come into real form. Then you'll eat your words.' There were more hoots and raspberries. The Gimp was making an obscene gesture with his right hand. Dougie felt himself getting hot under the collar. 'I bet he scores on Sunday and that the Hibs beat you!' That was it. He might as well have said that the sky had turned tartan and it was raining satsumas. 'Tell you what,' cried the Gimp, not interested in blood now, but total victory, 'Hibs win with Stevenson scoring, I'll wear green for the whole of next year and never talk about the Gers again.' He smiled at the others. 'And Rangers win, you give up supporting losers and join us.' Dougie felt like smashing his fist into the Gimp's heavy face but thought it would be like punching marshmallow. 'Okay,' he said, 'it's a deal.' 'Shake,' said the Gimp. 'No,' said Dougie, 'don't know what I might catch but it's a deal anyway.' He stormed out of the room with the others' laughter echoing in his ears.

'You're completely barking mad,' Billy had said later. 'Mental.' Dougie nodded. 'I know. I got angry.' For the next week, Dougie walked about the school, conscious of the amused stares and cat-calls of the Gimp and his friends, and also of neutrals, people who Dougie didn't even know, who had been astonished to hear a madman from S3 had claimed that the European champions were to be beaten by the Premier's bottom club from a goal by a Guatemalan 3rd Division player. Things were made worse in the Sports View of the *Daily Record* on Thursday where Alex Cameron had exclusively reported, under the headline **'Hosanna's Leith Nightmare'**, that the Guatemalan had had a nervous breakdown and barricaded himself in his flat, only emerging to post application forms for casual work on Caribbean cruise liners.

Dougie was to go to the match with his dad and Uncle Bobby who both lived now in Edinburgh. Because it was a

Sunday match, he travelled up by bus on Friday to spend the
weekend and maybe do some Christmas shopping. On the
Friday night his dad and Bobby took him out to the Old Toll
Bar, a right Hibee hang-out. The atmosphere, throughout the
place, was one of gloom and despondency. Little groups of old
men sat about crying into their beer. 'Aye,' said Uncle Bobby, 'I
can't see anything else but a real hammering.' Dougie told them
what had happened at school. His dad whistled. 'That was rash
son.' He took a sip of his pint. 'Jesus Hosanna Stevenson,' he
continued, bitterly, 'I've got more chance of scoring against
Rangers than he has.' Dougie looked at his father's beer belly.
Even taking that into account his dad probably did stand more
chance of scoring against Rangers than Jesus Hosanna
Stevenson. Bobby looked at the pictures on the wall, the big central one of the legendary Joe Baker, 1960. 'If only cloning was
at a more advanced stage,' he muttered. Dougie fell into a deep
depression. 'I'll just away back to the flat,' he said. 'No wait,'
said his dad, 'I'll just finish this.' Dougie sighed impatiently. His
father still thought he was eight. 'I know the way, I've been lots
of times.' 'Boy's got to grow up sometime,' said Bobby. His dad
gestured at the door. 'OK but straight home and don't talk to
any weirdos.' Dougie took a look round the bar. Bit late for that
kind of advice, he thought.

His dad's flat was between Junction Street and Leith Walk
and there was a short cut that involved going up an alleyway
and across a tiny bridge, skirted by derelict factories, all closed
in the '60s. As he entered the alley he could see the tall
stanchions of the floodlights at Easter Road. It had begun to
snow and he crunched along, his breath freezing in the air. He
wished there was some power, some authority that could
change things even just for a day, the kind of magic he used to
read about in books. He was nearly halfway across the bridge
over the railway when he realised there was someone standing
in the shadows, in the middle. He stopped, suddenly frightened,
then swallowed and walked faster, trying not to look at the
figure, which seemed to be that of a man standing stock still,
immobile. He made as if to hurry by.

'This is the place my dreams were made,' the figure said,
quietly. 'Now look at it.' A large piece of snow fell from his
cap, as he gestured, stiff-armed, in the general direction of the
stadium. He had moved, partly to block Dougie's way. 'Ah,
you're young. You still believe, don't you?' His voice was

gentle, almost wistful, though his heavy hand clamped on Dougie's shoulder. Dougie noticed a carton on the rail of the bridge beside him, a battered fish, untouched. 'Here,' the voice said. A large paper bag was being forced into Dougie's arms. Dougie tried to grab the package but the sudden weight of it surprised him and he spilled something. As he turned round, bending, to retrieve it, he heard the words, 'remember 1960'. When he stood up, the man had vanished. Dougie ran as fast as he could back to the flat, stopping only when he was at the door, in the full streetlight. As he reached for his key, he looked at the object he'd picked up. It was a battered old boot with leather ankle guards. Even though it had begun to snow quite heavily, he could make out a strange little yellow circle on the heel, with the initials J.B. J.B. Joe Baker.

When he woke the next morning, the boots were still by the bed. It hadn't been a dream. He had met Joe Baker's ghost and had his boots. It was a sign. If only he could persuade Jesus Hosanna Stevenson to wear Joe Baker's boots in Sunday's game, Hibs would win, the Gimp would be destroyed and the glory days would return to Easter Road. He spent Saturday morning searching for Jesus Hosanna Stevenson. Alex Cameron had mentioned he was holed up in a flat in Newhaven. With the precious boots in a bag, Dougie tramped the length and breadth of Newhaven looking for the Guatemalan. He thought it was going to be difficult till, down an alleyway, he came upon a door which bore a picture of the Guatemalan, exactly as it had appeared in the programme of the first match he'd played, except this time it had a dart through the head. There was an element of the Hibs support that could be cruel, reflected Dougie. He knocked, tentatively. He could hear a noise inside, some scratching, scuttling sound, then silence. He knocked again, louder, then called through the letterbox, 'Mr Stevenson. Can I talk to you?' Again there was silence. Dougie called again. 'I'm a Hibs supporter.' This admission was met by a sudden barrage of noise as though someone was dragging furniture along the floorboards, towards the door. 'It's OK,' reassured Dougie. 'I'm here to help!' 'GO-AWAY,' came a high-pitched scream from within. 'But Mr Stevenson,' Dougie persisted, 'I *am* here to help. Honestly.' 'Who helps me?' asked a suspicious voice from within. Dougie cleared his throat. 'Joe Baker,' he said. There was a pause and then a rattling of chains, the sound of locks and bolts being drawn before the door was drawn open a fraction. A frightened face peered out. 'He's dead,' it said. 'I know,' said Dougie calmly, 'and he asked me to bring you his boots.'

Jesus Hosanna Stevenson lived in a sauna. The central heating was up full blast and there were at least four other electric fires in his living room. He himself was wearing at least two woollen sweaters. Dougie fought against the overwhelming wall of heat and sat down at a chair the footballer had indicated. The Guatemalan stood across the room, tanned but tense. 'It's all right,' said Dougie. 'I come in peace.' It was the only thing he could think of saying but he didn't appear to take offence which was good because Jesus Hosanna Stevenson was holding a big baseball bat. Dougie explained the encounter as best he could, conscious of the fact that it sounded mad. To his surprise the Guatemalan interrupted him. 'What did this Joe Baker look like?' he asked. 'Don't know,' said Dougie, 'it was dark. But he didn't look like a ghost. He wasn't white or anything.'

'Good,' muttered Jesus Hosanna Stevenson, 'not a calleja then.' Dougie looked mystified. 'A calleja,' said the Guatemalan. 'A personification of another person's curse or spite. If you'd seen one of them you'd have known it. Takes a master occultist to make one that doesn't have gaps all over their face.' Dougie shook his head. 'I don't understand.' Jesus put down the bat and drew up a chair. 'Call it para-psychology, or magic,' he said. 'Take your pick. It doesn't matter. What matters is if you believe.'

It was quite the most confusing afternoon Dougie had ever spent. As much as he could keep up, Dougie understood that Jesus had been doing a doctorate at the State University when the clarion call from Easter Road had arrived. 'I'm a student,' he said. 'Played a bit of amateur football, but I couldn't believe it when I got the offer from Hibs. Do you think they confused me with Jesus Hosanna Johannsen, winner of the Guatemalan Golden Boots Award?' Dougie smiled weakly. Anything was possible with Hibs. 'Of course I didn't complain. A month's salary here is enough for me to complete my entire course. Thought all I had to do was play a few games then slide into obscurity. But I didn't count on two things.' 'What?' asked Dougie. 'The devilish cold. And the passion.' The passion was something Dougie did understand. 'It's life and death,' said Jesus. 'It's life after death,' whispered Dougie.

As Jesus was doing his doctorate on 'Magic and Ritual in

the Pre-Columban cults', not only did he believe Dougie's story but was prepared to act on it. 'Never mock the dead,' he said grimly. Two matters, however, remained unresolved. Jesus was sceptical if he could get the boots on and, more seriously, he wasn't even in the squad for the Rangers game. Dougie and he sat for a while in silence. The snow had begun again, the fresh wind from the North Sea scattering it across the windowpanes. Jesus shivered, made for the kitchen to make some cocoa. On the way he switched on the radio. He hadn't had time to switch on the kettle when the sports announcer had given the shock news that the majority of the Hibs team was down with food poisoning and Jesus Hosanna Stevenson's phone had begun to ring, urgently.

'Life is cruel,' his Uncle Bobby was saying later that evening, as he opened a can of Export. 'Just when we thought it couldn't get worse,' agreed Dougie's dad. 'They've even had to draft the Guatemalan in. Thought I might get a call myself. That's why I'm staying in beside the phone.' He shook his head, ruefully. 'It'll be 36-0 for sure.' Bobby nodded grimly. Only Dougie knew that the food poisoning epidemic – from battered haddock – was a master plan from beyond the grave. Later, when he went to bed, he rang the number Jesus had given him. 'Got them here,' Jesus had whispered. Dougie could hear the rustling of a paper bag. 'Good man,' whispered Dougie. 'But it's so cold,' Jesus whispered. 'It'll be red hot in Easter Road tomorrow,' said Dougie and put the receiver down before his dad heard.

On the afternoon of the match, however, even Dougie was freezing cold. The snow had worsened and they had a real job of it even walking to the game. Little knots of sad-looking Hibs supporters battled along against the elements while brand new coaches full of Gers supporters swept past, scattering them with slush and ice. It was like a Charles Dickens novel. Some-where on one of these plushly upholstered buses was the Gimp, savouring his victory already. Little did he know, thought Dougie. Little did he know. At the ground Dougie got a shock. Grant Brebner had recovered slightly and Jesus was on the bench. From his position behind the Hibs goal Dougie could see him, huddled forlornly under piles of coats. It was a setback but Dougie didn't have too much time or energy to worry because the snow had become a blizzard and was driving into their faces. He could hardly keep his eyes open. 'Surely cancel it,' said his dad, deep from beneath the protection of his Pride of Leith scarf. 'It's on SKY,' shouted Uncle Bobby, 'they'll play it if they can.'

From what Dougie could discern through the snow, the match had kicked off. He saw the orange ball skid immediately off someone's shin and into touch. It was clear that the conditions were impossible for football. Rangers took the throw. Even in these circumstances Rafael Domingo Sanchez looked a class act, skating effortlessly round three leadenfooted Hibs defenders before crashing the ball from 35 yards off the underside of the bar and, via the goalie's head, into touch for a corner. 'Rafael, Superman,' chanted the Gers supporters, somewhere off into the storm. They sounded muffled, as if they were singing behind a screen, which in a sense they were as the weather was worsening. Dougie thought of the Gimp's smug, pink face, grinning away inside his Designer Rangers Thermal Track and Combined Snow Suit. From the resulting corner, the ball swirled wickedly through the snow and round the post but not before there had been a nasty clash of heads involving Rangers' Michael Owen and Frank Sauzee. As the latter was carried off, the Hibs fans groaned. Jesus Hosanna Stevenson was getting stripped off, or seemed to be. It was hard to tell as he seemed to have fourteen different layers of clothes on. 'Oh Christ here's the Michelin Man,' someone said. 'What's he got on his *feet?*' someone else screamed. Jesus took the field wearing what appeared to be several pairs of tights and Joe Baker's boots. Took the field was actually rather a grand way of describing it for what Jesus Hosanna Stevenson was really doing was shuffling in a bandylegged and painful way towards the centre circle. The Rangers fans were killing themselves. By the time Jesus had passed the halfway line, the ball was back in the Hibs area, the keeper bravely saving at Sanchez's feet, snow-ploughing to the penalty spot. The Hibs fans applauded half-heartedly. It would appear that even in Arctic conditions the Hibs defence had more holes than a fakir's nightshirt. 'The only hope,' Bobby was saying, 'is the weather.' When the ball spun out in midfield, the referee consulted his linesman on the left, and the fourth official. 'He's going to call it off,' said Dougie's dad. Rangers took the throw. It broke to the veteran Pat McGinlay who took a speculative whack at the ball. It sailed over the Rangers bar. The referee wiped the snow from his eyes and for some reason only known to himself, gave a corner to Hibs. Through the pelting snow Dougie could see

Hibs lining up the corner. The referee was looking again at his linesmen and all three were shaking their heads. He had the whistle in his mouth. 'That's it,' said Bobby, stamping his feet to get some feeling back.

But it wasn't it. Unaware of the ref's intentions, Brebner ran up to the ball and scaffed it. It slithered eratically into the penalty area where it disappeared in a small snowdrift just outside the eight yard box. A defender took a vague whack at it, as you might if you were blasting a golf ball from a bunker. As Rangers players trotted in the direction of the intended clearance, the ball swerved back towards the penalty spot. Obligingly it stopped, as if trapped by some invisible foot, right in front of Jesus Hosanna Stevenson who had finally arrived in the area after a long and painful trek. The Hibs support, those who could see, gripped arms. The ground fell completely silent apart from the patter of the snow and the eerie howling of the wind. Jesus stopped and looked at the ball for a moment. Then, as Rangers players desperately sought to make up the ground, he drew back his right foot and let fly with Joe Baker's boot. The keeper, difficult though the conditions were, reacted with the instincts of a cat and sprang at the projectile bulleting towards the top left-hand corner of the net. He caught, gathered, and was still looking with astonishment at the old boot he was holding when the ball trundled over the line into the net. The Hibs end erupted and they didn't hear, or care about, the referee's whistle calling off the match for the wild howls of jubilation. Through a forest of clenched hands and waving arms Dougie could see Jesus Hosanna Stevenson being carried, beaming, off the pitch by team-mates and into legend.

Grinning and dancing, the three of them tripped home, through snow-blocked streets and gridlocked traffic, over the little bridge to his dad's flat. As they passed the spot where he'd got the boots, Dougie looked around. There was no-one to be seen, though for the first time Dougie saw, beyond the bridge past where the ghost had been standing, the wrought iron gates that stood in front of the old factory there. '**JOHNSTONE'S BOILERMAKERS**' it said, with, underneath, a little unmistakable logo still bearing flecks of yellow paint. He stood and laughed till the tears ran down his face while his dad and Uncle Bobby cuffed each other on the shoulders and thought how, in forty years of following Hibs, they'd never seen a victory so well celebrated.

Iain S. Mac a' Phearsain

MOLADH TEAGHLAICH

O, Fionnlagh Mòr
nise sin agad duine mòr tapaidh
's cho math air naidheachdan innse –
d' athair a bh' ann
an e?

chan e – mo sheanair
ach saoil
ma bha e cho math sin
carson a bhiodh sùilean a' bhodaich agam fhìn
a' tuiteam gu làr
's a chasan air chrith
fon bhòrd
nan cluinneadh e thu?

FAMILY PRAISE

Oh, Big Finlay
now there was a big strong man
and so good with the yarns –
your father
was he?

no – my grandfather
but I wonder
if he was as good as that
why would my old man's eyes
fall to the floor
and his legs tremor
under the tabletop
if he heard you?

ILE

Eadar Port Eilein agus ceann an rathaid
sìos dhan Oa
tha Eirinn cho teann ort
's a tha thusa orm fhìn
ann an dorchadas a' chàir
a' tighinn air fàire
ann an solas buaile na gealaich
ann am priobadh gaoil is briseadh dùil

ISLAY

between Port Ellen and the road end
down to the Oa
Ireland's as intimate to you
as you are to me
in the darkness of the car
appearing on the horizon
in the light of the moon's aureola
in a blink of desire and disappointment

nick E. melville

street seen

1

a distinguished gent
under a woollen cap
elderly elegant
grey
wears a fawn jacket
of corduroy
a leather patch
on each elbow
which swing
with an affluent swish

but
I see him

raking in bins
picking things

up
from the pavement

and checking for change
in phone boxes

unclaimed   for
gotten

2

pubescent girls
yearn for
pubessence boys

fleshy condiments
for their faces
and
puppymeat groins

fluidly mixedup by loins
they give birth to baby sisters

to get off

school and
adult lessons

3

a drunk man
on the bus is raving

he is older

methylated
alcoholed

he calls us all
animals

Uncivlised

and then extols
the values
of the Arab world

whatever that is

are you listening my friend?

4

I overhear a woman
middleaged
approaching
two younger females
and asking if they live here

they kind of share a laugh
but I can hear no more

I am intrigued

she stopped them
just like that

later

a man asks me
if I live here

I say
no

because I dont

for a little while

I think

I am being followed

5

a painted lady
a culting whore
with a pen
and clipboard
asked me
to be happy

what
I said
is there to be happy about?

she looked at me blankly
with her false identity
and laminated smile

I told her
she was just collecting money
to fill the sleazing pockets
of her pimping jesus bigamist

I did the christian thing

and told her to

Fuckoff

6

up the dead end
of a deadened alley
a toy dog sits

its leash abandoned
laid
upon the ground
of pock marked asphalt
riddled
with used condoms
worn and spent
rolled back into
packets of pavements

did a child leave it
or lose it
in this deviant street?

curious weeds fiddle with
cracks
in the walls of
derelict buildings

John Miller

EVENING IN THE CARPENTER'S COTTAGE

In your cherry, gold-sequined Amsterdam dress
and pink Portobello Road sandals, you sip
chilled vodka and brown American Coke
while I lounge in black, as if dressed for some
New York, downtown attic gallery opening,
in my Spanish boots, as Miles Davis' cool blue trumpet
strolls round the house with a walking bass;
in the belly of the oven steam mussels,
humming with garlic and lemon in blue sky shells
gathered from the low salt tide this very afternoon,
barnacled and orange and fat with seas
from half the world, which we will soon suck
and swallow, picking the pearls from our teeth
to stud our plates with their tiny treasure
as this tight crofter's night untangles,
candlelit with all the possibility of elsewhere.

ON THE ROAD HOME IT WAS SUDDENLY

On the road home it was suddenly
a night for driving with the headlights off,
adrift amongst the steady constellations
of crofts on the far side of the loch.

We'd switched the world off and sat
in the thrumming dark riding on trust
daring a little further, a little further
past deer grazing unstartled, hanging panes of light,

and I realise we're suddenly past
the difficult mechanism of learning to love
and through into that safe place where it rests
cooling and ticking, where it loses its noise

and complicated scenery and takes on
a deep forest background we barely notice:
its thick-leaved, pine-coned stillness,
its long growing, deep as summer heather;

only to be caught out turning a corner
and sun-stunned by a sudden long view
down the loch of what we now are.

So we glide on, out past the last house of doubt,
out into the hinterland of the rest of our lives,
switched off, still running.

Michael Munro

DANCER

In a green field
on a blue day
a little girl is dancing,
the arms down ramrod straight
the face like fizz,
for the step dance is serious stuff.
And across fifty years
and one wild sea
my mother still would dance
when the mood was on her.
I never was a dancer,
but it seems to me
there is fine love, and the fortunate may know it,
there is stark joy, and the best among us find it,
and we all go dancing at the end
into the bright west
dancing dancing.

Donald S. Murray

LANGUAGE

Gaelic was sewn into us like grains
of oats, turnip-seed, split potatoes
ploughs folded below earth each spring.

It took root among the small talk
villagers stacked at peat-banks
or found gleaming in green fields,

Or when the sharp blade of their tongues
cut through each crop of scandals
that was the season's harvest in some homes.

Yet now croftland lies fallow.
Winds keen through rush and nettle.
Cold showers of thistledown blow

White where potatoes stalked and blossomed
and the words of English broadcast on the air
find strange, new seed-beds on our lips.

WEAVING

Work warped his existence,
snarling up each hour he spent
checked within that room,

Days spooling into one another
until there was no pattern to his life
except that forming criss-cross on his loom.

A blur of two by two, four by four,
herringbone, plain or fleck;
these strands and shades that spun

Yarn tight and taut around him
as if he were a thread within the weave
of each tweed folded up and done,

And he'd pedal to escape its hold,
clicking quickly to break free
of all that snagged and held him;
both cloth and life's strict symmetry.

Stuart Murray

FRANK O'HARA HITS HAGHILL

It's twelve twinty in Dennistin oan a Friday.
Ah head east alang Alexandra Prade,
pass thi LEE RIGG, then
cross err it thi lights oan Cumbernauld Road.
It's wages day, so ah go intae thi newsagent next tae YOGI'S
(where we goat thi cheap pakora thit gied me the skitters)
    and buy ginger an some criss an sweeties.
Then al be roon thi coarner an intae yur close,
chappin thi door,
anah don't know,
mibbyul make toast.
Later wul go doon thi broken brick stairway
between hauf empty hooses an patchesa grass,
oantae Duke Street an intae the toon.
An ah know thit yul say
'*yoor gawny fuckin walk me tae death again,*
intye ya cunt.'

Liz Niven

KOSOVO SOUND WAVES

On the radio,
an Irish journalist
was talking of Kosovo.

Over there, researching,
she'd met a woman
who'd lost four children
in a cafe-bar massacre.

She talks of the sound,
of a dying child. A small *phew*.
The sound of your child dying
is a sound no-one wants to hear.
My own pale comparison,
years back, a six month foetus
stopped breathing.
Ultra sound thudded no heart beat,
only a dull machine whirr.

Three healthy children later,
I weep for this Kosovan mother;
running across towns,
desperate for shelter,
huddling in a cafe bar,
grenades and bullets follow.
Stench of burning flesh mingling
with coffee shop aromas,
formica tables no barrier.

The Irish journalist, herself
no stranger to violence,
her own nation familiar with
the dying child's sound.

Circling this globe are
weeping women,
tears enough to weave a flood,
drown out every sound on earth.

On the radio
an Irish journalist
tried talking of Kosovo.

Fiona G. Parrott

THE STRENGTH OF A SECRET

Balance on the pier.
Watch the missing board.
The splinters.
The lights.
Close your eyes tightly, now
listen
to the roll in the ocean's sigh.
Hear it keeping beat to
your own heart rhythm?
And the sun today –
it's nearly bright enough to
bring light down
below the surface.

See the seagulls?
Filling up the blue,
breaking through
this still, Russian air.

It looks so calm from the surface.
To break through that line,
separating life from life,
changing the current of today's
10 o'clock news.
Are the seagulls crying?

One hundred and eighteen Russian sailors
stuck on the tongue of the Barents Sea.
A soundless bed
of seaweed, silt
scars and skin.

But now the submarine's losing its pulse
to the nuclear weapons
aboard
alive
accountable.

This is the secret
wrestling Russia's pride
and the fact that
time is everything.
A hard lesson
when you find out too late.

Put your secrets through the gun barrel
and
       fire
           fire
                fire...

The seagulls have stopped crying
The secret is too loud.

Jo Ramsey

AFTER BIRTH

They part us too soon
but the bed is made ready
and even before they fold me
in papercrisp sheets, I sink
in drifts of dreamless sleep.

They bring you in at first light,
hooking me from sleep
by my barbed name,
hauling me up
to the surface of the day,

offering me the miracle
of you, five hours old,
one hot scarlet cheek blooming
in the guddled nest of quilts,
one dark seeking eye

renewing our acquaintance
of the night before
when the first sound you heard
was my subsiding roar,
our cries mingling

in an inhospitable room.
Solid in my arms
you feed in underwater light;
half-drawn curtains
fending off the sun.

Exhausted women lay
their massive breasts
against the pillows,
hoarding sleep
against the wakeful night,

drained by the immensity of love.
There is time enough:
this is the first of your life's days
and the years spread out like a cloth
patterned with rich and strange design.

Jane Rawlinson

OBSESSION

Obsession had hollowed out Grace. Shrinkwrapped skin on bone. Sucked her tinder dry. Kindled her insides until her eyes smouldered – almost as if she were possessed. Which, in a way, she was. She was two people in one. Like an old oak tree split by lightning. Or Siamese twins sharing the same heart. Loussa and Grace. Grace and Loussa. One, an old black woman nearing seventy, the other, a housegirl, still, after all these years. Within the compound, Grace, sullen in a pastel uniform. But when the gates clanged shut behind her? Out stepped Loussa into the street, strong and free.

'*Looser*?' asked Mrs Planter fifty-eight or nine years ago, looking at the awkward ten-year-old who clung to her mother's skirt. '*Looser*?'

'It means grace, Mem, in our language,' explained the mother, her newest baby heavy on her back.

'Then Grace she shall be!' The white woman waved her magic wand and so it was. All those years acting a part she hadn't chosen. Considering herself blessed.

Until along came Nelson Mandela. A black man as President. A black man in power. Which told her all things were now possible. She saw then how they had stolen her life. Worse, they had dispossessed her even of her name.

The night that the President was sworn in, she reclaimed herself. Became Loussa. Flowered within the sinuous, silky rustle of her name. Loved herself. Saw herself as their equal. On the wings of that name she soared above the one-roomed servants' quarters at the top of the rickety stone staircase behind the garage. Above the courtyard where the three sisters sat under the jacaranda tree, like the Fates endlessly respinning their lives. One day, Loussa promised herself, she would have her revenge. A life for a life. It was in the Bible. A life such as they had. That was her right. That's what she wanted. That was the promise of the politicians, the promise of the sisters themselves. 'One day, Grace, all this will be yours.'

And she'd earned it. When she first joined the Planter household, ten-year-old Grace thought she'd died and gone to heaven. That she was in the company of angels when she met the three little fair-haired, white-skinned girls for the first time.

When she saw the pantry crammed with food, the lush grass on the lawn, the sparkling bathrooms.

Now, in the sunset of her life, Loussa saw that she had never really been part of their world. She still lived in the same cement-floored room. Still cooked on a charcoal burner outside. Still bathed in a yellow plastic bowl under the tap behind the garage. And then she rejoiced quietly in the dilapidation of the house, the peeling paint and falling plaster, the enamel baths veined with rust. Times are hard, the sisters were fond of saying. Times are hard.

'We'd never manage without you, Grace, dear,' they said as often.

It was true. They couldn't. She stood between them and chaos. Put food in the larder. Clean underwear in their dressing table drawers. Tucked them into bed at night. Got them up in the morning. It dawned on her gradually, that she had them in her power. She frowned at them then. Obeyed orders slowly and when it pleased her. Watched them flounder in the fear of her displeasure. The terror that she might abandon them.

They started calling her Loussa, then. Added pleases and thankyous to their peremptory requests. Picked their own dirty underwear off the floor. Mopped up their spills. Offered her cast-offs and cups of tea.

Then they called in a man in a black suit. He sat at the oval mahogany table and wrote.

'Are you sure?' she heard him say. 'Are you quite sure? Are there no living relatives?'

'No,' they insisted. 'There is nobody. We are the last.'

Afterwards they showed her the piece of paper.

'All this will be yours, Loussa,' they sang, cooing over her like doves in their soft silk blouses. 'All this.' Their hands fluttered to indicate the house, the garden. Everything in them.

'As if a piece of paper means anything!' her family mocked her.

But Loussa knew. She had seen it for herself. She would live in a white man's house as Mandela had promised. She would live like a white man. After all these years! She stuck grimly to her task. It was worth it now. She had everything to gain.

Once the will was made, the sisters changed. Went back to calling her Grace. Loussa tried to block her ears to the sound that jarred up the stone staircase through the rockery, filtered through the frangipani and hibiscus. Told herself it was no more than birdsong. *Graaace, graaaace*. Persistent as the grate of the shrike. Drilling like a woodpecker into her skull, her brain, fit to drive her mad.

It was Miss Dorothy who reminded Grace she was older than they were. 'If looks could kill!' she said seeing the maid's alarm. And laughed.

Once the idea had been implanted in Grace's mind, the thought they might outlive her, wouldn't go away. It whined like a mosquito inside her skull. She increased their daily ration of poison. From a quarter bottle to a half. Then a pint. A quart. Sometimes she lingered, quite deliberately, in the street on her way home from the shops. Stopped to talk there, where they could see her from the upstairs windows. Where she could see them. Three white, drooling moon faces. Or she came with the heavy, clinking bag nearly to the gate, then turned away. Walked past. Hopped on a bus into town. Made them wait. Made them suffer.

Once she was inside the gate, they pounced. As jerky in their movements as early movie stars. 'Loussa, dear,' they trilled, ripping through the plastic. Saliva trickling. Hands in a wild St Vitus dance that was only calmed by the first drink. Their consonants sharpened by the second or third. A brief blossoming into wit and gaiety when she almost fancied she was doing them a favour. The sharp decline through senti-mentality to nightly oblivion. They depended on her all right. Couldn't manage without her.

Then came the letter from a distant cousin.

'Make up the spare bed, Grace, there's a dear,' said Deirdre, her vowels as sharp as ever her mother's had been.

With the 'Grace' ringing in her ears like a death knell, Loussa took down the spare sheets. She knew about blood ties. Knew what the sudden appearance of a cousin meant. Her heart pumped venom round and round her body till it sang in her ears and made the whole world spin. Tomorrow, he was coming. He'd come and they'd send for the man in the black suit. Nearly sixty years of slavery would be wiped out as easily as chalk from a slate. Unless, unless...

Loussa sat on her door sill in the dying light. With her spar-row's legs stuck out in front of her, calves in the dirt. At the end of them, her old green plimsolls pointed at the sky. Her toes peeping through. So she would lie in her coffin. Just so. But not yet. Not yet. In her right hand she held a cutlass handle. Her left hand ground the blade evenly against the sill.

'Graaace!' bleated a voice from below. 'Graaaace... where's my green blouse?' She didn't even bother to look out. She knew it was Miss Dorothy. Miss Dorothy who had once been her favourite. Whose blouse was where it always was, in the middle drawer of her dressing table.

The blade gobbled the last of the sunset. Glimmered blood red. The light went last from this highest point of the garden. Down under the tree it would be almost dark. The sisters pale as moths. The syllables of their speech merging like the shapes around them into an amorphous blur as they downed their gin...

Later, she would go down. Find them mouthing the same sucking, dribbling sounds they had made as babies. One by one she would lever them off their chairs. Across the yard. Into the house and upstairs. There, she would strip them. Manoeuvre their rag doll limbs into starched night-dresses. Tuck them in. Turn off the lights. All except the landing light that Mrs Planter said must always be left on in case one of them had a nightmare.

Then, she would come back for the knife. She tested it against the pad of her thumb. Grunted as a dark line welled like a fine brush stroke. It would do. Yes. It would do very well.

138

R.J. Ritchie

L ove
etter

Faint heart ne'er won ...

and so,

if *I* may be as **bold**

here is an outline

of *My feelings for You,*

there is no subtext

stated, *I* wish to <u>underline,</u>

i am not boxing clever

<u>with honourable</u>

you do not need

<u>indent</u> and with not

to read between the lines

a **shadow of doubt.**

but please please please you *MUST*

On noitɔɘlɟɘɿ and despite

Your shady background,

I think *I* am rightly justified

sign on the ....

in saying (without

s   t   r   e   t   c   h   i   n   g

the point), that *My* emotions are

centred

on *You* and if *You*

,etacorpicer ton od

My grief will drive *Me* to the **very** margin

of

n **d** *ing*

l **e** *aning*

s *liding*

sli **p** *ping*

f **a** *lling*

drown **i** *ng*

r **and very** pos**sibly**

right off the ed

James Robertson

RENÉ MAGRITTE IN EMBRO

As I wis gaun by Moray Place
I met a gent in bowler-hat
An overcoat, an mair nor that
He had an aipple in his face.

I trauchelt ower tae Royal Circus:
Leaves were birds, the birds were stane.
I heard a moothless wife mak mane:
'Wurds are symbols sent tae irk us.'

A German sausage in a helmet
Had aw the New Town leddies keekin,
For he wis baith a coorse an sleek yin,
An gart them twitch frae hem tae pelmet.

A muckle boolder in the lift
Wis floatin ower the gurlie sea.
Coffins on a balcony
Were no impressed. They didna shift.

The toun lay in the mirk black nicht
As I gaed on tae Charlotte Square;
A torso, tuba an a chair
Hung in the air sae blue an bricht.

An artist lad on Princes Street
Wis drawin croods wi chalk an wiper.
Says he, 'Ceci n'est pas un piper',
An signed himsel 'Rennie Mackay'.

I daunert syne by Randolph Crescent,
Whaur clootie-heidit luvers bide.
The trees were fittit oot inside,
An aw the hooses arborescent.

An at a hoose by Telford's brig
It seemed the neibourheid wis tense:
An aipple'd taen up residence,
An it wis green an affie big.

On Belford Road I had a seat,
Tho it wis in a bonnie bleeze.
The blocks were blawin in the breeze.
I left ma shuin inside ma feet.

A broken landscape on the flair,
A path across the canvas gress.
I stude forenent the windae gless,
An saw a view that wisna there.

I passed the Dean an gaed in ben,
For it wis rainin businessmen.

Laurna Robertson

ARCHIVE: BUDAPEST

This is the shirt he liked to wear
for an afternoon stroll
to the city square
on a Sunday.

This is the hole the bullet tore
through the back of the shirt
he always wore
on a Sunday.

These are the threads,
beginning to fray,
where a young wife rubbed
dark bloodstains away.

This is her room,
this is the drawer
where she hid for so long
the shirt he wore.

These are the neighbours
who might have spied
on visitors
the day he died.

Those are the cousins
who didn't dare mention
the shirt she kept hidden
and lose her a pension.

Here is the shirt
she has kept to show
how her husband was shot
so long ago
with the friends he met
in a leaf-strewn Square
one Sunday.

This is all
that's left of the day
a bullet
took half her life away
on a Sunday.

Dilys Rose

MILK TEETH *800 BC*

Observe cut marks in the ring
of neckbone where my head
was severed from my body.
Note that the milk teeth
embedded in my jawbone
show no sign of cavities.
Deduce that my head once hung
above the entrance to the cave
as a gift, an offering, a charm.
State composition of the rope
which lashed my scalp to the roof.
List constituents of the midden.
Chart the order in which I rotted.

Now imagine me alive, at play.

Rosie Russell

POEM FOR MY DAUGHTER – 1

I never met my daughter.
She went away in a grey cardboard bedpan –
the type convenient as fruitbowls for visitors
    embarrassed with grapes –
covered by a handtowel;
disposable, municipal green.

No introduction between frantic buzzers
and hastily pulled curtains.
Our only greeting the silence of ceased pain.

A life too brief for baptism or burial –
no name to call.

And when I looked for her
she had already gone
in the hands of a retreating nurse.

No knowing whose chin, whose eyes they weren't to be.
The nurse I would know anywhere.

Steve Sankey

PEREGRINE

It's mid June, and I get lucky:
She hasn't seen me, and the falcon
Leaves a tail-stream of vapour to her eyrie,
Of feathers
            feathers
                        feathers.

Carrying prey,
She calls and clatters into the mess,
Into a shock of shrieks,
No doubt where this eyrie lies.

She plucks and feeds
                  plucks and feeds
                                    plucks and feeds,
Attends three chicks.

Smoky feathers drift across
                        drift across
                                    drift across,
And, as I walk away,
A family of wrens
Falls from the hill like heather seed.

146

Ian Stephen

FISH-SOUP – A RECIPE

You take a large wooden fishing boat which has been too good at catching small fish and so starving other fish and seabirds. You don't worry. *Fear Not* because this scale of hunting has within it the seeds of its own destruction. You wait until it's been decommissioned from fishing and is being broken up with chainsaws and diggers. You reserve large pieces of oak – the breasthook, ribs... and set aside. You maintain a small boat, using that oak from the larger one where necessary, to replace parts. Conserve the sawdust. Set aside. You source ballast stones, from the Baltic coasts, in the same way that Baltic traders came in ballast to Stornoway. Dumped their stones here to take instead the weight of whitewood barrels packed with herring. Left behind a small islet they call Little Russia. And some folding-money. The cash is gone but some of the smooth stones are left.

You've been to the Baltic. German side. Former-East. East is a relative measure. You've taken some more smooth stones back home, a continuity of trade. This ballast lends stability to that same smaller, older boat. In winter you line up the land-marks you were shown as a spotty kid. They still work. You find a reef and lower lures made from old chrome: car-door handles; offcuts from pramwheels. Mackerel or squid bait sends out a slick from a trailing hook. You fish the drift, over and over the reef and wait out the cold on the hands. Wish you'd brought more socks, thicker clothes. But the tugging comes and then the verdigris shape of the cod. Its changing colours on the bleached stones. Then the shoal of green and white coalfish grows beside the cod, on the ballast.

You gut the fillet in one, down the backbones. The white of the cod, grey of the coalfish is placed in brine. Oak dust from the decommissioned *Fear Not* is set on a steel tray over a meths burner. It's from a Danish version of a fondue-set. This *Fear Not* was built in Denmark. The oak sends up pungent smoke. Bricks collected from the demolitions of Rugen (the same source as the ballast stones) are built, dry, around the burner. The stiff fillets are placed on a grid spaced from the burner but in the smoke. The whole assembly is closed with a stainless-steel hood found on yet another shore. The tideline of Tolsta, Lewis, the village which claimed the name of *Fear Not* for its boats. First a clinker wooden beach-boat, powered by a lug sail and a second cousin of your own small surviving old boat. Then the favoured Tolsta name was transferred to progressively larger vessels. Until you had the powerful, Danish-built hull. A fine vessel in herself but misused by chasing the sandeels and pout which should have fed the cod, the haddock, the puffins and gannets and migrating sea-trout. Which made good money from fishmeal suppliers and mink-food wholesalers.

Now the remains of the massive hull are smoking the white-fish which still shoal on the reefs they can't yet drag. Sufficient oak dust for sufficient smoke to curl, hidden, into the fillets. They cool. They are set aside along with the stock made from boiling the cod's head and the backbones of the coalfish.

This is shopping. Some people do this on Saturday after-noons instead of going fishing. You source red onions and white ones, fresh dill and parsley. Scottish butter. Should it have been Lurpak? Equal quantities of each? Desiree potatoes.

You peel rose skins to show waxy yellow and the faintest tinge of green. Onions move towards the transparent, in the butter but maintain the integrity of pink and white. Wax cubes join them and the first of the smokies. You mustn't be in a hurry to add the stock. A little of the greenery now to infuse flavour but most of it reserved to yield fresh green speckled with pepper over the remaining flaked fillets. Not before you've balanced the dish with full-cream milk and some extra cream.

The soda-bread in rounds, to be broken to steam when the close of the song signals. Taste for seasoning. *Fear Not*, it'll be OK.

Edward Stranger

streams entering Loch Lomond at Balmaha

snake
streams
through
shallows.
serpents
slip
slither
slip
slither
slide
to
the
fat
water
of
the
loch

Ruaraidh MacThòmais

CRIOMAGAN

Criomagan beatha ann an clach
a thuit bho Mars bho chionn fhada
a' dùsgadh bheachdan
bho àrsairean is luchd-saidheans,
is criomagan cuimhne
a' dùsgadh ann an seann inntinn:
mòinteach is muir,
cuilean is caileag,
eich is eachdraidh,
ceòl is cailleach,
is mìle cuspair
a' gluasad 's a' fannachadh.
Tha ar beatha cho toinnte
's cho gluasadach
ris an t-saoghal iongantach
a tha fàs 's a' seacadh
gun fhaochadh,
's chan eil air ach feuchainn
ri cumadh
a chur air na criomagan.

FRAGMENTS

Fragments of life in a rock
that fell from Mars long ago
stirring up theories
from archaeologists and scientists,
while fragments of memory
waken in an old mind:
moor and sea,
puppy and girl,
horses and history,
music and old women,
with a thousand topics
rising and falling.
Our lives are as intertwined
and as mobile
as the marvellous world
that grows and withers
incessantly,
and we might as well try
to shape
the fragments.

GUTH

"Nach eil a thìd' agad sgur
dhe do rabhdaireachd?" –
guth
a thàinig thugam ás a' bhalbhachd.
Uill, chan eil mi cinnteach.
Co ás eile thigeadh an guth,
agus nach ann anns a' bhalbhachd sin
a tha na facail am falach
's ag iarraidh a thighinn an uachdar?
Cha robh ann ach plòidh,
cuireadh bho na facail
a thighinn gan iarraidh,
is fhios aca
nach èirich iad 'nan aonar,
gum bi iad a' mireadh ri chèile
is uaireannan a' milleadh,
ach a' sìor ghluasad,
a' lorg 's a' lorg
's a' togail.
Is mar sin thuirt mi ris a' ghuth,
"seo do rabhd
's bidh dùil ri tuilleadh".

A VOICE

'Isn't it time you stopped
your versifying?' –
a voice
that came to me from the dumbness.
Well, I'm not quite sure.
Where else would the voice have come from,
for surely it is in that dumbness
that the words hide
and they want to surface?
It was just a dodge,
an invitation from the words
to come and fetch them,
knowing
they do not rise unaided,
that they interplay
and sometimes interfere,
always moving,
searching, searching,
rising.
So I said to the voice
'Here's your verse
and expect others.'

Valerie Thornton

A SELFISH POEM

We all have to thank you
for going now and quietly.

We, who have known you
half out the window
two floors up
and determined,
thank you for not going
that way, for not crushing
the spindly roses
and scrubby grass below.

We, who have seen you
in Lady Macbeth's nightdress
race barefoot through
the small hours streets
shrieking in terror
from the wardrobe mirror,
thank you for stopping
on the living room carpet.

We, who have woken
to glass breaking
with the dawn
as yet another vodka bottle
which was never yours
went out your window,
thank you for going
without smashing a thing
except, perhaps, your glasses.

We, who have answered
your wails for help
from a pool of drunken blood
on the close landing,
thank you for leaving
so little mess behind
your closed door.

And we, who opened
your door that Sunday
(with the key you kept
behind the storm door)
to your shrilling smoke alarm
and a wide-eyed cat,

we, who turned off
your cauliflower florets
(boiled black)
and your smoking chicken leg
with you on the settee,
oblivious, before *EastEnders*
(the omnibus edition),
cannot thank you enough
for going, alone and gentle,
and not taking us
with you.

Dawn Wood

LIKENESS

The way she sits, resigned
reminds me of my family's pale-eyed
women. Her mind
will be busy as she trades the rain
for a trinket
distraction while driven.
She is always naive and she knows it
a second too late as she sifts
through her money in front of a stranger
trying to find something appropriate;
always surprised how this gaze
is reflected, now from the fourth
generation she has known.
She forgets each one bargains
to run from the previous,
looks at her watch as her mother did
– wrist tipped,
bones too near the surface.

BIOGRAPHIES

Margaret Beveridge was born in Kirkintilloch and now lives in Edinburgh where she is a community and adult educator. She has published some dull but worthy pieces in professional journals and writes reviews for the *Edinburgh Food Guide*, but this is her first published piece of fiction.

Nick Brooks is thirty-three, and has lived in Glasgow, Manchester and northern Spain. He has had a variety of occupations, from shelf-stacker to security steward, and has just finished a degree in English. Currently, he's doing a Masters in Creative Writing at the Edwin Morgan Centre.

Paul Brownsey lives in Bearsden. He was once a newspaper journalist and is now a philosophy lecturer. He has had stories published in most Scottish literary magazines and regular collections, including the New Writing Scotland collection, *Some Sort of Embrace*.

Tom Bryan was born in Canada, 1950. Long resident in Scotland, he lives in Selkirk. A widely-published and broadcast poet, short story writer and novelist, his work has appeared in several previous editions of *New Writing Scotland*.

Leanne Bunce is presently studying towards a PhD in Critical & Creative Writing. She writes poetry and short fiction. She began submitting work for publication in June 2000. *Western Charm* is the fourth poem she has had accepted this year. She's also had a short story accepted for publication by The Women's Press.

Larry Butler is a Californian living in Glasgow since 1981, teaches Tai-Chi, started the Poetry Healing Project and Survivors' Poetry Scotland; worked in London as director of PlaySpace Trust, Matchbox Theatre, co-director Drama Therapy Centre. He has recently completed a feasibility study for Greater Glasgow Health Board on the idea of Arts on Prescription, and is helping to create an eco-village.

Ron Butlin's work has won several SAC Book Awards. He was Scotland's writer-representative at the British Council's *Oradea 2000* in Romania. He recently completed poems for a violin-and-voice concerto for Radio 3. A regular journalist for the Sunday Herald, he lives in Edinburgh with his wife and their dog.

K.M. Campbell is a retired solicitor, born and educated in Glasgow and now settled in Perthshire. His first novel, *Winter of the Eagle* (1980), gained a Scottish Arts Council Book Award and was followed by *Honours of War* (1981). The hiatus was occasioned by professional commitments but he is writing again.

Stuart B. Campbell has been published in numerous journals and anthologies. Shortlisted for the Poetry Society/BT e-Poet Laureate Award, 2000. Publications: *Robie Gow's Prison* (1996); edited the anthology *Things Not Seen* (1999). New collection *Navigation For Innocents* to be published by Dionysia Press in Spring 2002.

Michael Chromy works in Glasgow as a teacher. He is married with two young sons. His work was first published in *West Coast Magazine* in 1990.

Ian Crockatt was born in Perth in 1949. His collection *Flood Alert* was published by Chapman in 1996, and *Original Myths*, a 14 part poem with etchings by Paul Fleming, was published by Cruachan Publications in May 2000. His next collection, *Cries from a Clearing*, will be published by Peterloo Poets in Spring 2002.

Loren Cruden was born in the United States in 1952 and now lives on the Isle of Skye. Her nonfiction books include *The Spirit of Place*, *Coyote's Council Fire*, *Compass of the Heart*, *Medicine Grove* and *Walking the Maze*; and poetry appearing in *Gairm* and *A Little Borderless Village*.

Criosaidh Dick is a writer of teenage fiction and history books, broadcaster, and retired lecturer in Gaelic and Celtic Studies at Strathclyde University. She also farms Blackface sheep and Highland cattle. Gaelic is her first language. Born Glasgow, 1934, and educated at Glasgow University.

John Duffy is a Glaswegian now settled in Huddersfield. He is a member of the Albert Poets who run workshops and performances in West Yorkshire, and is employed as a bibliotherapist by Kirklees Libraries. His third collection, *The constancy of stone*, appears this year.

Magi Gibson, poet and short story writer. Lives near Stirling. Widely published in anthologies and magazines. Shortlisted in 2001 for the Asham Short Story Competition. Collections include *Kicking Back* (Taranis), *Strange Fish* (with Helen Lamb, Duende), and *Wild Women of a Certain Age*, (Chapman). RLF Writing Fellow at Paisley University.

Rody Gorman – Collections: *Fax* (Polygon 1996); *Cùis-Ghaoil* (diehard 1999); *Bealach Garbh* (Coiscéim 1999) and *On the Underground* (Polygon 2000). Working on collections in English, Irish & Scottish Gaelic; anthologies of 20th century European poetry in Gaelic and of 20th century Irish and Scottish Gaelic poetry; collection of haiku and PhD on Donald MacAulay's poetry. SAC Writing Fellow, Sabhal Mòr Ostaig 1998-2001, Writer-in-residence, University College Cork, 2002.

Charlie Gracie is originally from Baillieston, Glasgow, and now lives with his family in Thornhill, near Stirling. He works with homeless people in Clackmannanshire. Writing short stories and poetry, he has had work published recently in *Twa Dugs*, *Pushing Out the Boat* and *Poetry Scotland*.

Yvonne Gray lives in Orkney with her family. Her poems have appeared in *Rationed Air* and in *NWS 18*, *Poetry Scotland* and *Cenrastus*. Recently she collaborated with film-maker Tim Fitzpatrick on *Between the Terminals*, a short film based on one of her poems for the 2001 St Magnus Festival.

Francis Green was born in Northampton, England, in 1977. Moved to study English Literature at Glasgow University in 1995. Francis is a songwriter and musician in the band 'animation' and runs a small record company. He is currently working on a collection of short stories from which *Beautiful* is taken.

Roddy Hamilton lives in Aberdeen. He has had fiction published widely in Scottish anthologies and literary magazines and has been broadcast on Radio 4. He has also written for the stage and short films. He is currently working on a novel and making a collage out of Smarties.

George Inglis lives in Houston, works in Glasgow and studies part-time at the Edwin Morgan Centre for Creative Writing. Previously published in *New Writing Scotland* and *Shorts 3*.

Gordon Kennedy – writer and electronic musician. Won several prizes for music and poetry, including the 1999 RLG International New Writers Competition. He is interested in developing forms which trace these two disciplines to a common root, and particularly in the possibilities of electronic media. Website: www.organica.co.uk

Born in Sutherland, **Ian McDonough** now lives in Edinburgh. Widely published in Scotland and beyond. Poem sequence *A Rising Fever* published 2000 by Kettilonia, first collection *Clan MacHine* published Oct 2001 by Chapman. Convenor of Edinburgh's Shore Poets, co-edited their anthology *The Ice Horses* (Scottish Cultural Press). SAC Writers Award 1999. He has just completed a series of poems on particle physics for Strathclyde University.

Morag McDowell was brought up in Glasgow, lived and worked in Frankfurt, Munich, Brighton and now Ayrshire. Her stories have been published in various magazines and anthologies. Achievements include the Macallan/Scotland on Sunday short story awards (joint winner 1992) and the Brian Moore/CWN short story awards (runner-up 2000).

Suzanne McGruther was born in 1977 and brought up on the west coast of Scotland. She is currently studying for the MLitt in Creative Writing at Glasgow and Strathclyde Universities, and is working on a full-length novel. *Skin Deep* is her first published story.

Rob MacIlleChiar: born in Argyll, educated in Oban, Glasgow and Sabhal Mòr Ostaig. Worked in crofting, forestry, outdoor education, and IT. Currently writer-in-residence at Sabhal Mòr. Poetry published in *Westword*, *Poetry Scotland*, *An Tarbh*, *Northwords*, *Gairm*. At present working on a collection of verse in Scottish/Irish Gaelic.

Tony McLean was born in 1966 and has had various jobs in Glasgow, Tighnabruaich, London and Cheltenham. He has been writing novels and short stories for about seven years. This will be his first published piece.

Anne MacLeod lives on the Black Isle and has published two poetry collections, *Standing by Thistles* (SCP 1997) and *Just the Caravaggio* (Poetry Salzburg 1999 – recently reprinted). Her first novel *The Dark Ship* appeared in May from 11:9.

Hugh McMillan teaches in Dumfries. His poetry and prose have been widely published in book form and in magazines and anthologies in Scotland and abroad.

Iain S. Mac a'Phearsain was born and raised on the Canadian prairie in a family of Skye and Islay descent. Educated at universities in Alberta and Nova Scotia, he taught French Immersion in high schools before coming to live in Skye where he is a Gaelic lecturer at Sabhal Mòr Ostaig.

nick E. melville is a young poet, previously published in: *Five Leaves Left* (Neruda Press), *Cutting Teeth*, *Product*, *Poetry Scotland*, *Nerve*, *Lallans*, *The Herald*. nick E. has produced and performed two shows at the Edinburgh Festival Fringe for Pleasance Theatre: *The Post Off Poems* and *Spoke Out: poetry stand up*.

John Miller lives and works in and around Ullapool in Wester Ross. He has had a range of poems published in a variety of Scottish magazines and is currently daring to think aloud about his first collection.

Michael Munro was born in Glasgow in 1954, works as freelance editor and lexicographer. Stories and poems in various anthologies and magazines. Play and story broadcast on Radio Scotland. Author of *The Patter*, *The Complete Patter*, and *The Crack* (All Canongate/Birlinn).

Donald S. Murray comes from the Isle of Lewis and is now an English teacher in Sgoil Lionacleit, Benbecula. His collection of short stories, *Special Deliverance*, was published by Scottish Cultural Press and shortlisted for a Saltire Award. His poetry has been widely published both in previous issues of *New Writing Scotland* and elsewhere.

Stuart Murray has just graduated from Printmaking at Glasgow School of Art. He won the Royal Scottish Academy's W. Gordon Smith Award in March 2001. Previous work has appeared in *Cutting Teeth* magazine. He was born in 1978 and lives in Glasgow.

Liz Niven – born, educated, graduated in Glasgow. Writer, poet, currently resident in Galloway via Easter Ross. Has held posts in Dumfries & Galloway as Scots Language Dev. Officer & Writer-in-Residence. SAC Award 1996. Recent poetry, *Stravaigin* (Canongate 2001) and, for Education, *Turnstones 1* (Hodder & Stoughton 2001) A recent commissioned work for the Year of the Artist, *the bit remnant left* interpreted the impact of Foot & Mouth in south west Scotland.

Fiona G. Parrott recently graduated from the Creative Writing course at the Universities of Glasgow and Strathclyde. Her poetry has been published in *Poetry Scotland* as well as various anthologies. She has just completed her first novel, *Tangerine Blues*, and currently studies for her PhD at the University of Glasgow.

Jo Ramsay was born in 1952. Worked as medical librarian before becoming television archivist for ITN and later the British Film Institute. Has lived in Stromness since 1988. Poetry published in *Chapman*, *NorthWords* and *Cutting Teeth*; one small collection by Gladragon Press. Short stories also published. Received Scottish Arts Council bursary in 2000.

Jane Rawlinson has been living and writing in Scotland since 1980. Writer in residence, (Scottish Arts Council) Grampian Healthcare 1994-6. Convenor, Scottish PEN Writers in Prison Committee. Four published novels drawing on experiences of living and working in Kenya and Iran. *Obsession* was written after visiting southern Africa in 1998 and 1999.

R.J. Ritchie has been Secretary and Treasurer of the Stirling Writers Group since 1993. Employed to produce environmental magazines. Regular contributor to Letters page of *The Scotsman*. Poems published in a wide range of Scottish and English magazines (including *Chapman*, *Cencrastus*, *Lines Review*, *Envoi*) and several minor competition successes.

Laurna Robertson taught in Primary and Secondary schools in Fife, Edinburgh and Berwickshire. She now lives in the Scottish Borders. Her work has been published in *Lines Review*, *Orbis*, *Other Poetry*, *The Scotsman*, *Smith's Knoll*, *Shetland Life*, *New Shetlander* and *New Writing Scotland*. *The Ranselman's Tale* was published in 1990.

James Robertson is a fiction writer, poet and editor. Published work includes a short story collection *The Ragged Man's Complaint*, a novel *The Fanatic*, and poetry collections *I Dream of Alfred Hitchcock* and *Fae the Flouers o Evil: Baudelaire in Scots*. He lives in Fife.

Dilys Rose has published two collections of poems, three of short stories – most recently *War Dolls* – and a novel, *Pest Maiden*. Currently working on a second novel, as well as short fiction and poetry. She lives in Edinburgh.

Rosie Russell is an ex aid worker, teacher and mother of four young boys writing occasional poetry and working on first novel in the Highlands.

Steve Sankey combines his poetry writing with his post of Chief Executive of the Scottish Wildlife Trust, and farming on the Carse of Stirling. The natural world inspires his writing, and to-date he has had poems published in *The Herald*, *Zed 2 0*, and the RSPB's magazine *Birds*. He is an active member of the Stirling Writers' Group.

Ian Stephen was born in 1955 on the Isle of Lewis. Graduated from Aberdeen University. Worked for 15 years in the Coastguard Service. Resigned in 1995 after gaining the inaugural R.L. Stevenson award. Two SAC bursaries. Poems and short stories published in many countries. Artwork widely exhibited. Main current project – fiction indebted to oral storytelling.

Valerie Thornton writes poems and short stories. She has been shortlisted for the SoS/Macallan Prize, and has also published an award-winning creative-writing textbook, *Working Words* (Hodder). Her first collection of poems, *Catacoustics* (Mariscat) was published in 2000. She is currently Royal Literary Fund Fellow at Glasgow University.

Derick Thomson (Ruaraidh MacThòmais), born Isle of Lewis 1921. Studied at University of Aberdeen, Emmanuel College Cambridge, Bangor (North Wales). Taught at Universities of Edinburgh, Aberdeen and Glasgow (Professor of Celtic, University of Glasgow 1963-91). Published seven collections of Gaelic poetry with many English translations.

Dawn Wood grew up in County Tyrone and graduated in 1986 from Queens University, Belfast, with a degree in Microbiology. She subsequently moved to Dundee and works as a university lecturer, teaching science-based subjects. She is married with three children. She has been attending a local writers' group.